Confronting Eating Disorders

ISSUES
(formerly Issues for the Nineties)

Volume 24

Editor

Craig Donnellan

 *Independence*

First published by Independence
PO Box 295
Cambridge CB1 3XP
England

British Library Cataloguing in Publication Data
Confronting Eating Disorders – (Issues Series)
I. Donnellan, Craig II. Series
616.8'526

ISBN 1 86168 155 0

Printed in Great Britain
The Burlington Press
Cambridge

Typeset by
Claire Boyd

Cover
The illustration on the front cover is by
Pumpkin House.

CONTENTS

Introduction

Confronting Eating Disorders is the twenty-fourth volume in the **Issues** series. The aim of this series is to offer up-to-date information about important issues in our world.

Confronting Eating Disorders looks at eating disorders, body image and obesity.

The information comes from a wide variety of sources and includes:
Government reports and statistics
Newspaper reports and features
Magazine articles and surveys
Literature from lobby groups
and charitable organisations.

It is hoped that, as you read about the many aspects of the issues explored in this book, you will critically evaluate the information presented. It is important that you decide whether you are being presented with facts or opinions. Does the writer give a biased or an unbiased report? If an opinion is being expressed, do you agree with the writer?

Confronting Eating Disorders offers a useful starting-point for those who need convenient access to information about the many issues involved. However, it is only a starting-point. At the back of the book is a list of organisations which you may want to contact for further information.

*****

Eating disorders

Information from the Florence Nightingale Hospitals

Dieting or, at the very least, watching what we eat has become a way of life for many of us. For some, what originally appear to be 'normal' concerns about weight and staying in shape evolve into severe preoccupations with food, weight and body image. The result is sometimes an eating disorder, of which there are two important syndromes: anorexia nervosa and bulimia nervosa. Overeating or compulsive eating can be defined here too.

Definitions

Anorexia nervosa

Anorexia nervosa is characterised by deliberate weight loss and a refusal to eat, often leading to the point of emaciation. Anorexics are so afraid of gaining weight they will stop at nothing in order to stay slim. Unfortunately, anorexics never reach their 'ideal' weight. They always have just a few more pounds to lose. Regardless of how thin anorexics become, they still perceive themselves as fat.

Often anorexia starts with normal dieting but, instead of stopping when the desired weight is reached, it continues until the person is actually underweight, often by an alarming amount.

Some anorexics binge and purge food but maintain a low body weight. The sufferer may hide food to avoid eating it and take laxatives and slimming pills to assist their weight loss.

Although the word 'anorexia' actually means loss of appetite most sufferers of anorexia nervosa have a normal appetite but dramatically control their urge to eat.

Bulimia nervosa

Like anorexics, bulimics are obsessed with food and weight. However, as opposed to not eating, bulimics often binge eat and then purge themselves to avoid gaining weight. During the binge, bulimics eat large amounts of food, very rapidly and with little self-control. Purging may involve vomiting, using laxatives or excessive exercise. Despite this cycle, bulimics are usually average weight, or slightly overweight.

Bulimia usually affects a slightly older age group of women in their early twenties. Unlike a woman with anorexia, a bulimic woman often manages to keep weight within normal limits. This behaviour usually causes feelings of guilt and this feeling then results in comfort eating again and so it goes on.

A previous history of anorexia nervosa is evident in about a third of patients presenting with bulimia.

Both anorexics and bulimics may experience serious and dangerous physical complications as a consequence of the disorder.

Compulsive overeating

Compulsive overeating or binge eating disorder is rather like bulimia. It is characterised with a loss of control and distress about the binge eating behaviour. These episodes may occur when alone at night and may be associated with loneliness, unhappiness and loss of self-esteem. Unlike bulimics, compulsive overeaters do not utilise compensatory mechanisms such as vomiting or purging to control their weight and as a consequence are likely to become overweight.

Obesity

Obesity is often part of one's constitution and is not necessarily a problem of psychopathology. Overeating that has led to obesity as a reaction to distressing events, such as bereavement, accidents, operations may be followed by 'reactive obesity', especially individuals predisposed to weight gain. Obesity can dent self-confidence and result in emotional distress.

Who develops an eating disorder and why?

Both anorexia nervosa and bulimia nervosa commonly begin during early adolescence, coinciding with the onset of puberty. However, an eating disorder may strike as early as age eight and as late as middle age.

Although many reports suggest that eating disorders are more common in individuals raised in middle- to upper-class homes, eating disorders are not restricted to any specific class or culture. They are however much more common in affluent Western society and rare in third world countries.

Ninety per cent of those with eating disorders are adolescent and young adult women. One in 100 young women develops anorexia, two or three in 100 develop bulimia. Adolescent boys and young men may be affected more rarely.

Eating disorders affect about 60,000 people in the UK.

It is often difficult for others to understand what would provoke a woman to starve herself or to purposefully vomit after eating. Theories developed to explain the emergence of eating disorders usually regard these illnesses as the result of a combination of biological, psychological and social factors.

Biological

It appears that genetics may predispose a person to an eating disorder. But once an eating disorder develops, there are several biological changes that might result in the intensification of the illness. For instance, the self-starvation of anorexics may lead to chemical changes that dull a person's feelings of hunger or result in feelings of depression or sadness. In addition, it is believed that vomiting can chemically induce feelings of euphoria or light-headedness that some bulimics may seek to mask feelings of anxiety or depression.

Psychological

A variety of psychological factors are likely to influence the development of an eating disorder. These may include:

Perfectionism

People with anorexia nervosa often place high expectations on themselves and are self-driven.

Self-esteem

Many anorexics and bulimics report feeling worthless.

Rigid thinking

Individuals with an eating disorder frequently report dealing with life in the extreme. Everything is black or white, there is no grey area.

Control issues

Many people with eating disorders report a fear of lack of control over their lives or environments. Anorexics may say that their restricted eating is their way of sustaining control.

Sexuality

A significant number of anorexics and bulimics have had traumatic or negative sexual experiences, such as childhood sexual abuse.

Other psychiatric disorders

Eating disorders frequently coexist with other psychiatric illnesses such as depression. In addition, those individuals struggling with bulimia nervosa appear to be at a greater risk for alcohol or drug abuse problems.

Social

A variety of social factors play a role in the development of eating disorders. The excessive value that is placed on thinness in our society can lead women to believe that their self-worth depends on their body size or appearance. Thinness becomes equated with achievement, intelligence, popularity and success.

It can be difficult to tell the difference between someone with an eating disorder and someone who is simply very weight conscious in this age of fitness, health and dieting

---

This may lead to a persistent struggle to create the 'perfect body'.

It has also been suggested that an individual's family life may affect a child's risk of developing an eating disorder.

How can you tell when concerns with food or weight have become a problem?

Many sufferers are defensive and secretive about their eating disorder.

There are several warning signs that indicate that a person's concerns with food or weight may have become severe enough to be considered an eating disorder. It can be difficult to tell the difference between someone with an eating disorder and someone who is simply very weight conscious in this age of fitness, health and dieting. Awareness of the following warning signs may alert you to either the presence or the possible development of an eating disorder.

Extreme weight loss or thinness

Preoccupation with food, weight or calories. Some people with eating disorders report being unable to hold a conversation without discussing food or weight.

Frequent weighing

Excessive concern about appearance and attractiveness.

Distorted eating patterns

Skipping meals, eating in secret, frequent binges, strict dieting, ritualistic eating habits.

Disappearing after a meal, suspected vomiting, or use of laxatives or diuretics.

Complaints of feeling nauseated or bloated after ingesting normal amounts of food.

In addition to these food-related symptoms, there are a variety of other characteristics and behaviours, which might also be present:

- Perfectionism.
- Rigid, inflexible routines.
- Withdrawal from friends or activities.
- Low self-esteem.
- Alcohol or drug abuse.
- Impulsivity.
- Mood swings.
- Manipulative behaviour.

The need for treatment

If left untreated, eating disorders can result in serious complications and even death. One thousand women die each year of anorexia. Medical complications from eating disorders may include:

Anorexia nervosa
- Cardiac abnormalities
- Cessation of menstruation/periods stop
- Anaemia
- Excessive body hair
- Osteoporosis
- Gastrointestinal problems
- Yellowing skin
- Hypothermia
- Dehydration

Bulimia nervosa
- Erosion of tooth enamel
- Menstrual irregularities
- Tearing of the oesophagus
- Anaemia
- Gastrointestinal problems
- Ulcers
- Enlargement of the salivary glands
- Electrolyte imbalance

Treatment

There are several different types of treatment for eating disorders; each type will be appropriate for one person but perhaps not so suitable for another. The type of treatment will also depend on the type of eating disorder, how severe the condition is and how much the sufferer recognises that they have a problem. Often the person themselves will deny that they have an illness and will therefore be unwilling to accept help. Also any treatment must be aimed at the underlying cause for the condition as well as trying to correct the abnormal eating behaviour.

Treatment for eating disorders generally has three goals:
- Correction of medical problems associated with starving or binge eating/purging.
- Resolution of the underlying psychological and social dynamics that contributed to the development of the eating disorder.
- Establishment of normal weight

and healthy eating behaviours.

Depending on the severity of the eating disorder, this may take different forms:
- Self-help groups
- Individual therapy
- Group therapy
- Family therapy
- Out-patient, day-patient care or hospitalisation may be recommended.

Depending on the individual, treatment may involve behavioural strategies to help develop better eating habits, psychotherapy to address any underlying issues which have contributed to the eating disorder, or medication to help correct any chemical imbalances that may be affecting behaviour or mood.

The first step is to help the sufferer recognise that they have an eating disorder problem. There may be guilt about their eating disorder and they will go to great lengths to hide it and deny it, although they are often relieved when they finally have to admit to having the condition.

The individual should be encouraged to seek help, initially from their GP, who will probably then refer to a psychiatrist or psychologist who will talk to them and assess the severity and type of eating disorder. An individualised programme of treatment will then be suggested.

Overeating behaviour requires an approved cognitive approach and order eating techniques to become stable to regain control. Subsequently, the person may need continued help to lose weight.

If you are a relative or friend

Unfortunately, it is often difficult for people with eating disorders to acknowledge that they have a disorder. They may not believe there is a problem, or they may not want treatment for fear it will involve gaining weight. If you believe someone you know is struggling with an eating disorder, there are ways you can approach this.

Be honest, state the behaviours you have noticed and what you suspect.

Know where help is available.

Regardless of the specific treatment chosen, simply acknowledging a problem with food or weight can be a big step toward recovery. If you suspect you know someone who is having difficulties with their relationship with food, or are unsure whether your concerns about weight and food are problematic, you may need to ask for help.

• The above information is from the web site of the Florence Nightingale Hospitals which can be found at the following address: www.florencenightingalehospitals.co.uk

© The Florence Nightingale Hospitals

Worries about weight

Information from the Royal College of Psychiatrists

Most of us, at some time in our lives, feel unhappy about the way we look – and try to change it. There are lots of ways of doing this. Changing the shape of your body is one that people often try. Many of us have an idea of the size and shape we would ideally like to be. Being smaller, shorter, or less well-developed than friends or brothers and sisters can make us feel anxious and lacking in confidence. So can being teased about size and weight – which is, unfortunately, common.

Our ideas about what looks good are strongly influenced by fashion and our friends. For example, you might compare yourself with the pictures of women in fashion magazines. Compared to them, you might worry that you are fat even if your weight is normal for your age and height. In fact, the women in fashion magazines are often unhealthily thin. There is actually quite a wide range of sizes and shapes that are within the normal, healthy range. If you're interested, there are tables showing normal height and weight. Ask your school nurse, doctor or library. Your weight, like your height and looks, depends a lot on the type of build your family has.

Staying a healthy, normal weight

Our bodies need regular nourishment to stay healthy and strong. This is especially important in the teenage years, when your body is growing and developing. A healthy diet should include all the things you need to develop normally – proteins, carbohydrates, fats, minerals and vitamins. Cutting out things you might see as fattening – such as carbohydrates and fats – can stop your body from developing normally.

There are some simple rules which can help you to stay a healthy weight. They sound quite easy but might be more difficult to put into practice. You can ask your family and friends to help you to stick to these rules – and it might even help them to be a bit more healthy!

- Eat regular meals – breakfast, lunch and dinner.
- Include carbohydrate foods such as bread, potatoes, rice or pasta with every meal.
- Eat at roughly the same time each day. Long gaps between meals can make you so hungry that, when you do eventually eat, you eat far more than you need.
- Get enough sleep.
- Avoid sugary or high fat foods and junk foods. If you have a lunch of crisps, chocolate and a soft drink, it doesn't feel as if you're eating very much, but it will pile on the pounds. A sandwich or roll with fruit and milk or juice will make you feel more full, but you are much less likely to put on weight – and it's better for your skin.
- Take regular exercise. Cycling, walking or swimming are all good ways of staying fit without going over the top.
- Don't pay too much attention to other people who skip meals or talk about their weight.

If you follow these suggestions you will find it easier to control your weight, and you won't find yourself wanting sweet foods all the time.

Miracle cures – do they work?

There seems to be a new one of these almost every week. Sadly, they often do more harm than good.

- Crash diets don't help you to keep your weight down – in fact, they may make you put on weight after a few weeks. At worst, they can actually be dangerous.
- Exercise helps – but it's got to be regular and increased only gradually. Too much exercise, or too much too soon, can damage your body.
- Laxatives may help you feel less guilty and bloated. Unfortunately, they don't reduce weight and can upset your body chemistry.
- 'Slimming pills' can't make you thinner. They might make you feel a bit less hungry, but unfortunately they can also harm your health.

Common eating problems

Problems or pressures at school, with friends, or at home, are common. People who feel pressured often find it affects their appetite. Some people lose their appetite if they are worried or tired. Others turn to food for comfort. This can lead to eating more than our bodies need, and can make us put on weight. Then it's easy to start worrying about getting fat and we find ourselves eating even more to comfort ourselves. It becomes a vicious circle. 'Comfort foods' often contain a lot of fat or sugar. Sweets, biscuits, chocolate, cakes and pastries are favourites. It can be helpful to keep a diary of what you eat to make sure that you don't slip into this.

If you are unhappy or stressed, it can be easy to focus on your weight and eating habits instead of dealing with the things that are bothering you. If this goes on for long enough, you can find yourself developing an eating disorder. The commonest eating disorder is becoming over-weight – or obesity. Other eating disorders are less common. Anorexia nervosa and bulimia occur most often among girls, and are discussed below.

If worries have altered your appetite or weight, it will help to talk to someone about it. You should ask your school nurse or doctor if you are worried about your eating habits and weight.

Signs of an eating disorder

With anorexia nervosa you will feel you are fat and will avoid eating, even though you aren't actually overweight. When you eat, you feel guilty and fat. So you avoid food, lose a lot of weight and become extremely thin. Strangely, the *thinner* you get, the *fatter* you feel! We don't fully understand why this happens, but it certainly makes the eating disorder harder to overcome. People with anorexia usually remain very active and say they are quite well, even though they become so thin that they avoid undressing in front of other people, or wear loose clothes which hide their size. Anorexia nervosa can be dangerous if it gets out of control. If you are a girl and you find that your periods have stopped, this is a danger sign which means you need help right away (this won't happen if you are on the pill – so if you are, don't wait for this).

If you don't eat much, you can feel as though you are starving! You may then find yourself bingeing – you eat lots and lots of food very quickly. Bingeing also happens in an eating disorder known as bulimia. In bulimia, foods like chocolates, cakes or biscuits are avoided, except during binges. Bingeing makes you feel fat, guilty and ashamed. You try to get rid of the food by being sick or using laxatives. It usually doesn't make much difference to your weight, but can damage your health and take up a lot of time and energy. Some people have both anorexic and bulimic symptoms.

Getting help

If you are worried about your weight or feel you may have an eating disorder, you should get some help.

You could start by talking to a family member, teacher, school nurse, counsellor, social worker, or your family doctor.

Your family doctor or practice nurse is the best person to give you basic information and advice on diet and weight. If you need more specialist help, they can refer you. They may suggest that you see a

If you are unhappy or stressed, it can be easy to focus on your weight and eating habits instead of dealing with the things that are bothering you

professional at your local child and family mental health service. This is a team of specialists including child and adolescent psychiatrists, psychologists, social workers, psychotherapists, and specialist nurses. They will respect your wishes for confidentiality and will be able to help you to regain control of your eating and weight.

Sources of further information

• Bryant Waugh, R. & Lask, B. (1999) *Eating Disorder: A Parent's Guide.* London: Penguin. This book is useful for young people as well as parents.

• ChildLine provides a free and confidential service for children.

ChildLine, Freepost 1111, London N1 OBR. Telephone 0800 1111. Website www.ChildLine.org.uk

• The Eating Disorders Association provides information and advice. Youth helpline 01603 765050.

• Youth Access offers information, advice and counselling throughout the UK. 19 Taylor's Yard, 67 Alderbrook Road, London SW12 8AB. Telephone 020 8772 9900.

• The *Mental Health & Growing Up* series contains 36 factsheets on a range of common mental health problems, including discipline, behavioural problems and conduct disorder, and stimulant medication. To order the pack, contact Book Sales at the Royal College of Psychiatrists, 17 Belgrave Square, London SW1X 8PG. Telephone 020 7235 2351, ext. 146; fax 020 7245 1231; e-mail booksales@rcpsych.ac.uk.

• The above information is an extract from the Royal College of Psychiatrists' web site which can be found at www.rcpsych.ac.uk

© Royal College of Psychiatrists

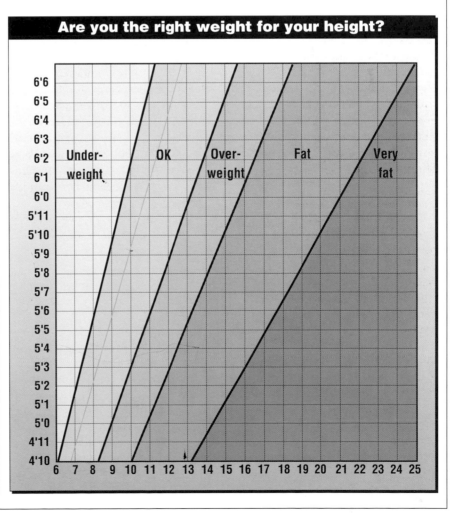

The children who starve themselves to cope with school

The image of super slim fashion models and celebrities is blamed for the rise of 'slimming diseases' in children and teenagers. But are other culprits at work? Here we look at the role stress at school is playing. By Elizabeth Hartley-Brewer.

The one result just about every secondary and the occasional primary school can be certain of as examination fever sweeps the country is an increase in the incidence of eating disorders among its pupils, girls and boys. As the pressure mounts, the pounds will drop off. For many vulnerable students, the stress associated with exams, and with GCSE and A-levels in particular, is known to trigger either the onset or the reappearance of anorexia nervosa and bulimia nervosa.

Is the concurrent increase in academic pressure and eating disorders merely a coincidence, with the main causal culprit lying on the pages of fashion magazines, or is there a connection? There is no national database of out-patient referrals, only of in-patient admissions, so any evidence that we are in the grip of an epidemic, especially at a sub-clinical level of disordered eating, is based on research samples and anecdotes.

The most often quoted figures on rates of incidence are those collated by the Eating Disorders Association, in 1994. The Association states that the rate is one in 500 in state schools, one in 100 in girls' independent schools, one in 55 among young women at university and one in ten in dance and drama schools. But Steve Bloomfield, the EDA's press spokesman, admitted the rates are probably twice that now, in each category.

Certainly, most of those who work in the field are convinced the problem is growing, in two directions – up in terms of absolute numbers and down in terms of age – and there are now more boys, pushing the ratio from one in 10 to one in eight.

Dr Dee Dawson, who runs the Rhodes Farm specialist eating disorder clinic for school-aged children in north London, said, 'We are certainly seeing more of it than ten years ago'; but not everyone is so certain. Dr Quentin Spender, a child psychiatrist in Chichester, is more circumspect, and thinks that some of the current apparent increase could be explained by greater awareness, especially among parents and teachers of younger children. However, he agreed that 'there's probably more of it now than in the fifties and sixties'.

Teachers are equally divided. The headmistress of the selective girls' independent secondary school, Oxford High, Felicity Lusk, said, 'We have always had a problem with girls and eating. I'm not sure it's getting worse, but it may be because people are coming forward earlier and with greater confidence. Currently, we have three or four girls in every year of 84 that we are actually working with, who are receiving medical attention, but we have quite a few more we are concerned about.

'Many girls seem to flirt with anorexia. It's how they cope with what they have to manage. I have also spent 20 years in the maintained sector, and I saw the same amount.'

On the other hand, Helen Storey, head of Silverdale, a mixed comprehensive school in Sheffield which is top of the local league tables,

admitted that it has become a new issue for many of their sixth form girls facing exams, and they have watched it build up. Overall, Sheffield is seeing four new community referrals for eating disorders every week among the 16 pluses – 200 a year – but the problems begin much earlier, and there's no local, NHS, in-patient eating disorder service for the under 16s.

Ms Storey believes that expectations, pressure and low self-esteem explain what she is seeing. 'A lot of it is what the girls expect of themselves and what's expected by others. Staff say, have a bit of fun, but there's the government pressure and things like the modular form of A-level, so the pressure counts. One of the most disturbing things is the self-mutilation – cutting and scratching – that we recognise as an early sign.'

Lusk views today's students as 'a generation under stress. From the moment dot they are geared up for their future career, going to the right nurseries, schools then universities. I don't think the league tables have helped. When we were top, it put enormous pressure on the staff and the girls, and parents can choose the school for the wrong reasons.'

As a GP based in north London, Dr Laurence Buckman is able to see a wider picture. He has patients who attend many of the central and north London selective schools, and believes school, and parental, pressure have a lot to answer for. 'The expectations at these schools are very high, and they exert a high degree of control over the girls. If they don't get 10 A stars, they think they're a failure.

'They have often got parents who are quite demanding. Where parents buy the education, they control that too, so the only thing left in the world these girls can control is their weight. Certain schools have a noticeably higher number.' Dr Spender said, 'Some girls need an excuse not to do well. Anorexia's a way out of the rat race without losing face.'

But the problem is not exclusive to the selective, private sector. All Sheffield schools can appoint up to three school-based learning mentors

to work with children experiencing learning problems under the government's 'Excellence in Cities' project.

Silverdale has one, not because the students are truanting but because of growing stress. Sue Porrill is an experienced school nurse. 'In this school, the concern is health issues arising from expectations. I'm looking at mental health, stress, family problems, breakdowns and beneficial and non-beneficial ways of coping.

'I'm worried that it's happening to boys too, though their friends won't talk. They're now becoming more conscious of their appearance, and work out instead. There are also eating disorders in schools in very deprived areas, where family problems are more acute. Poverty affects self-image too.'

Chris Dark agrees. He's head of Peers School, a mixed comprehensive on the Blackbird Leys estate in Oxfordshire. 'It isn't as acute a problem here as in schools where there is a collective compulsion for students to do their best. With more working-class girls, it's more a question of body image. Peer pressure's at the root.'

So the causes are multiple and can be complex. Marilyn Boulos is school counsellor at the high-achieving, fee-paying Haberdashers' Aske's School for Girls. She says that the pressure builds up slowly, and you can't really say that's the single cause. 'Every case is different. You can only ask each child what the balance is between home issues and school pressure. It's partly responsible; it's more probably a culmination of the academic pressure they're under, low self-esteem and family issues, which can be huge. Personality is also relevant. The girls who develop disorders are very bright,

highly sensitive, they like to please and they're perfectionists. Their work's always so neat.'

This last point was strongly reinforced by Rhodes Farm's Dee Dawson. 'These schools are selecting girls who are already perfectionistic and obsessive before they get there. These children always want to be best. You can't blame the schools. It's nothing to do with them that 50 per cent of all school girls say they are dieting at any one time. They see very skinny girls in the media. If they get thin, they get more attention from friends and believe people will like them more. It makes them feel good, and then they can't stop.

'Girls also use dieting when they have problems because it's something they can control. They are children who would probably end up seeing a psychiatrist. If they weren't dieting, they'd find other ways to take control. Their self-esteem is low. Many of them have major problems at home. It's never as simple as dieting gone wrong.'

The Eating Disorders Association literature confirms this: 'Eating disorders develop as signs of inner emotional or psychological problems. It is a coping mechanism for difficulties, used to block out painful feelings.'

But, accepting the association with self-driven perfectionism, does it really only come from the child? Dr Quentin Spender believes some of the pressure to be perfect may have been internalised earlier. One family claimed their 13-year-old daughter pushed herself to become the academic star, the Grade 7 musician, and the able sportswoman that she was, yet they pinned her school report on the wall, so who was she doing it for?

Young people who need to please may lose sight of who they are, and those who think they are not worthy to eat will have lost any positive sense of themselves. Indeed, several people described children disintegrating, psychologically and physically, in front of their eyes. Perhaps the culprit is not so much commercial image as self-image and, within that, identity itself.

Dr Mervat Nasser, consultant

psychiatrist, author and cross-cultural eating disorder specialist, talks of the importance of connectedness, of links to community and in establishing identity. She sees pointing the finger at fashion and being slim as 'very simplistic. It's not a cause but a correlation. It's not really the answer. Girls in traditional Muslim families in Bradford are more prone to eating disorders than those in more Westernised families because they experience more conflict with their gender role and sexuality.

'They're told by their successful fathers to work hard, do well and grow up; but not to go with boys, and to be feminine like their non-working mothers. If a girl achieves for herself, she's fine, but if she does it to please

---

'Eating disorders develop as signs of inner emotional or psychological problems. It is a coping mechanism for difficulties, used to block out painful feelings'

---

others, she gets confused and is not fine.'

There are no simple answers to what is a very complex problem. Each individual's relationship with food is intensely personal and encompasses their culture and

history. But if academic pressure is contributing in any way to the misery, or even uncertainty, experienced by some of our children, we should at least be debating it. And at the very least, we should know the scale of what is going on.

• Rachel Bryant-Waugh and Bryan Lask, *Eating Disorders: a parents' guide* (Penguin, 1999). Elizabeth Hartley-Brewer is author of *Motivating Your Child* (Vermilion, 1998) *Self-esteem for Girls: 100 tips* and *Self-esteem for Boys: 100 tips*.(Vermilion, Sept 2000).

• This article first appeared in *The Independent*, May 2000.

© *Elizabeth Hartley-Brewer*

Men get eating disorders too

Information from the Eating Disorders Association

Eating disorders are illnesses that are generally believed to affect young women, and not young men. Actually eating disorders can affect people of both sexes, all ages and all backgrounds. Research shows that approximately 10% of people with eating disorders are men.

How eating disorders develop in males

There seems to be less cultural pressure on men to be slim although the 'sixpack' shape and image may be important. The start of an eating disorder in males usually has a specific trigger. These include:

• Avoiding childhood bullying/teasing for being overweight
• Bodybuilding/exercise
• Specific occupations including athletics, dance, horse racing etc.

Young men find it hard to acknowledge or even recognise they have an eating disorder and then equally difficult to seek help. For example, weight loss is more likely to be attributed to physical causes rather than to psychological ones. Because of issues like these, young men's problems can be more difficult for professionals including GPs and psychiatrists to diagnose.

Eating Disorders Association

In a recent survey the majority of the men interviewed reported that their eating disorders had started in their school years when they were overweight and called names. Several reported being severely overweight in their younger years for a variety of reasons, mostly to do with low self-esteem, crises at home, pressure to do well in school, and difficulties with coming to terms with their situation. For example, one man was 10 stone at 10 years old and was put on a 'diet' by the school. This led to him eating on his own and subsequently being teased.

The particular pressures in the adult gay male community to have the 'body beautiful' were mentioned by the gay men interviewed. Some gay men talked about the conflicts they had experienced when younger.

It was felt to be a bigger and more common problem in the gay male community than has previously been acknowledged.

Men also experienced particular difficulty discussing their illness with their friends or relatives. One young man commented: 'It is more difficult to come forward, you cannot admit to your feelings in a macho culture; people think you are weak and you fear that you are going to lose respect from your friends.'

As with all eating disorders, the important issue is to seek professional help as early as possible, if this is difficult then the helpline service of Eating Disorders Association can certainly provide more information and a listening ear.

For help with eating disorders including anorexia and bulimia nervosa contact:

Eating Disorders Association, First Floor, Wensum House, 103 Prince of Wales Road, Norwich, NR1 1DW. Tel: 01603 621 414 (helpline – open 9.00am to 6.30pm weekdays) 01603 765 050 (youthline callers 18 & under – open 4.00pm to 6.00pm weekdays). E.mail: info@edauk.com Web site www.edauk.com

© *Eating Disorders Association 2000*

High-flying schools put girls at greater risk of eating disorders

By Kate Watson-Smyth

Girls at successful schools are more likely to succumb to anorexia than those who attend lower achieving colleges, a specialist in eating disorders claimed yesterday.

The 'hothouse' atmosphere of leading schools makes the students feel under more pressure to succeed and can trigger eating problems.

Sandra Passmore, a specialist in eating disorders at Birmingham Local Education Authority, said: 'I have worked in selective, non-selective and private schools throughout Birmingham and although there are problems in all types of schools, they are more marked in the most successful ones'.

'There are lots of factors that contribute to eating disorders but we know that being an anorexic takes a lot of discipline. Girls who are very academic can lose themselves in their work to take their minds off how hungry they are.'

The most recent data on the number of anorexics among female students was gathered by the Eating Disorders Association in 1994. It found that there were one in 500 sufferers in state schools, one in 100 among girls at independent schools, one in 55 at university, and one in ten at dance and drama schools.

But a spokesman for the association said the numbers had probably doubled in each category over the past six years.

Diane Cook, a clinical nursing specialist at the Woodbourne Priory Hospital, in Birmingham, said she had counselled girls from some of the top public schools in the region who weighed just five stone. Pupils were under more pressure than ever to succeed and there was a dangerous link between academic excellence and the quest for an impossibly thin body, she said.

'Girls are working incredibly hard, far more so than boys and often harder than they actually need to.

'Their whole self-worth is based on academic success and I believe there is a connection between over-achievement and over-dieting.'

Elspeth Insch, the head of King Edward VI Handsworth (Girls') School, Birmingham's highest achieving state school, said she believed up to 10 per cent of pupils had 'lower level' eating problems which she defined as girls being thinner than they should be and regularly skipping meals. She blamed female peer pressure for the increase in eating disorders.

An added concern was that many of the students' parents were themselves successful professionals who worked long hours and did not have time to ensure their daughters ate a proper meal every night.

Felicity Lusk, the headteacher of the selective girls' independent secondary school, Oxford High, Oxfordshire, said: 'We have always had a problem with girls eating.

'We have three or four girls in every year of 84 that we are actually working with, who are receiving medical attention, but we have quite a few we are concerned about. Many girls seem to flirt with anorexia. I have also spent 20 years in the state sector and I saw the same amount.'

Dee Dawson, the medical director of Rhodes Farm, a specialist clinic for school-aged children with eating disorders in north London, said it was not the schools that caused the anorexia but the fact that girls who were already the type to fall ill often ended up at high-flying schools.

'They come from high-achieving families and have decided they must keep up with their parents or brothers and sisters and either the pressure is already there or they put it on themselves.

'There are always several other factors, such as parental neglect, abuse, divorce and so on, which trigger it, but they are also very disciplined and if they decide to diet they will stick to it.'

Definitions

Information from ANRED – Anorexia Nervosa and Related Eating Disorders, Inc.

Anorexia nervosa: the relentless pursuit of thinness

- Person refuses to maintain normal body weight for age and height.
- Weighs 85% or less than what is expected for age and height.
- In women, menstrual periods stop. In men levels of sex hormones fall.
- Young girls do not begin to menstruate at the appropriate age.
- Person denies the dangers of low weight.
- Is terrified of becoming fat.
- Is terrified of gaining weight even though s/he is markedly underweight.
- Reports feeling fat even when very thin.
- In addition to the above, anorexia nervosa often includes depression, irritability, withdrawal, and peculiar behaviours such as compulsive rituals, strange eating habits, and division of foods into 'good/safe' and 'bad/dangerous' categories.

Bulimia nervosa: the diet-binge-purge disorder

- Person binge eats.
- Feels out of control while eating.
- Vomits, misuses laxatives, exercises, or fasts to get rid of the calories.
- Diets when not bingeing. Becomes hungry and binges again.
- Believes self-worth requires being thin.
- May shoplift, be promiscuous, and abuse alcohol, drugs, and credit cards.
- Weight may be normal or near normal unless anorexia is also present.
- Like anorexia, bulimia can kill. Even though bulimics put up a cheerful front, they are often depressed, lonely, ashamed, and empty inside. Friends may describe them as competent and fun to be with, but underneath, where they hide their guilty secrets, they are hurting. Feeling unworthy, they have great difficulty talking about their feelings, which almost always include anxiety, depression, self-doubt, and deeply buried anger.

Binge eating disorder: sometimes called compulsive eating

- The person binge eats frequently and repeatedly.
- Feels out of control and unable to stop eating during binges.
- May eat rapidly and secretly, or may snack and nibble all day long.
- Feels guilty and ashamed of binge eating.
- Has a history of diet failures.
- Tends to be depressed and obese.
- People who have binge eating disorder do not regularly vomit, over-exercise, or abuse laxatives like bulimics do. They may be genetically predisposed to weigh more than the cultural ideal (which at present is exceedingly unrealistic), so they diet, make themselves hungry, and then binge in response to that hunger. Or they may eat for emotional reasons: to comfort themselves, avoid threatening situations, and numb emotional pain. Regardless of the reason, diet programmes are not the answer. In fact, diets almost always make matters worse.

Anorexia athletica: sometimes called compulsive exercising or activity anorexia

- The person repeatedly exercises beyond the requirements for good health.
- May be a fanatic about weight and diet.
- Steals time to exercise from work, school, and relationships.
- Focuses on challenge. Forgets that physical activity can be fun.
- Defines self-worth in terms of performance.
- Is rarely or never satisfied with athletic achievements.
- Does not savour victory. Pushes on to the next challenge immediately.
- Justifies excessive behaviour by defining self as a 'special' elite athlete.
- Compulsive exercising is not a recognised diagnosis as are anorexia, bulimia, and binge eating disorder. We include it here because many people who are preoccupied with food and weight exercise compulsively in attempts to control weight. The real issues are not weight and performance excellence but rather power, control, and self-respect.

Body dysmorphic disorder

- Not yet an official psychiatric diagnosis, but may achieve that status soon.
- Affects about two per cent of the people in the United States.
- Strikes males and females equally. Seventy per cent of the cases appear before age eighteen.

- Sufferers are excessively concerned about appearance, body shape, body size, weight, perceived lack of muscles, facial blemishes, and other perceived body inadequacies and flaws. They continue to be concerned in spite of reassurances from friends and family members who usually can see nothing to justify such intense worry and anxiety.

- In some cases BDD can lead to steroid abuse, unnecessary plastic surgery, and even suicide.
- BDD is treatable and begins with an evaluation by a mental health care provider.

Please note: ANRED information is not a substitute for medical treatment or psychological care. For help with the physical and emotional problems associated with eating and exercise disorders, talk to your physician and a competent mental health professional.

Distorted perceptions

People suffering with an eating disorder often have a distorted perception of their body and personality

'What I think of me . . . I'm fat . . . I'm a horrible person . . . I must deserve this . . . It's my own fault . . . My problems don't matter . . . Others don't deserve an eating disorder, but I'm different . . . '

It is all too common for people living with anorexia and bulimia to have a mild to severe distorted perception of themselves. What is seen in the mirror isn't reality, and when they compare their physical or personality attributes to others they are extremely judgmental of themselves. A person suffering with anorexia or bulimia may see another person and think 'I wish I could be as skinny as them' and in reality, may actually be thinner. They may wish to be as smart, as funny or as compassionate as another person that they are equally as good as – the bottom line is that they cannot see their own good traits, especially in comparison to others, because of the low self-esteem they have of themselves.

A good example of a distorted perception is black and white thinking . . . Thinking that bad situations or feelings are the complete end of the world, and good situations or emotions are as bright as the sun. There is no stability or 'normalised' thinking with a middle ground, but harsh swings from one extreme to another. Combined with this is irrational behaviour that is not okay for others, but okay for the person suffering with the eating disorder.

An example would be: 'when I eat I am just a horrible awful person and deserve to die, but when I don't I am the best little girl in the world'.

A lot of times, men and women suffering with an eating disorder unfairly personalise the actions around them. They may think that everything someone says or does in some way is a reflection of them. For example: if during a group conversation one individual walks away to go to the bathroom, the person suffering with the eating disorder may think 'they left because I was acting stupid again'. There is also the feeling that 'everyone hates me', or only hangs around because they feel sorry for them, or are just being polite. Compliments are seen as polite gestures, but not truly compliments, and are often met with an invalidating remark about themselves. For example: someone compliments on a victim's achievement and they reply, 'no really, I'm so stupid. You

---

A person suffering with anorexia or bulimia may see another person and think 'I wish I could be as skinny as them' and in reality, may actually be thinner

---

should have seen how badly I screwed up last week . . . '

Victims of eating disorders take on unfair burdens of control for the world around them. They may feel responsible to make the world a better place, to want to cure the ills of everyone, and when they can't, punish themselves with self-hate remarks and actions. There is often a strong need to control their own lives and the lives of people around them, and when they cannot, they think it is unfair and take it out on themselves.

Self-blame can be another aspect . . . the victim may blame themselves for everything bad that has ever happened to them, believing that in some way they deserved it: e.g., 'my parents abused me because I was a horrible kid'. On the contrary, they may also blame others for everything and take no responsibility for their own lives. For example: 'if you'd been there for me, I wouldn't have purged'.

People living with anorexia and bulimia have a hard time being optimistic about any aspect of a situation or their lives. Everything seems negative in one way or another, or they only pick the negative to focus on. In comparison to others, someone else who achieves something is considered great, but the same achievement for themselves would be met with negativity and how it could have been done better. Though the world is not seen as perfect and others are not expected to act as such, the person suffering with the eating disorder may have high expectations of perfection for themselves.

Ultimately, one of the biggest perception distortions of the anorexic or bulimic is that 'life will be better and I will be happy when I lose the weight'. There is a false sense of control that is achieved during self-starvation/restriction, a feeling of comfort when bingeing, or a

---

People living with anorexia and bulimia have a hard time being optimistic about any aspect of a situation or their lives

---

temporary release of emotions and guilt during purging . . . In reality none of the above has been achieved

except in the victim's perception. There is no light at the end of the tunnel of an eating disorder, even though victims may think there is. In reality, the only true light comes from recovery.

• The above information is an extract from the Something Fishy Web site on eating disorders which can be found at www.something-fishy.org

© Reprinted with permission from Something Fishy Music & Publishing. 1996-2000

Common misconceptions

Below are some of the most commonly held misconceptions about the behaviours attributed to anorexia, bulimia and compulsive overeating

'I cannot be anorexic because I do eat when I have to . . . '
Restriction of food and calories does not mean complete restriction for every victim. For some this means restricting certain types of foods (each victim sticking with what they perceive as 'safe foods') and limiting calories to below normal on a daily basis. For others this means fasting for a certain number of days and then eating 'normally' for the next number of days, and repeating the cycle continuously.

'I don't fit any category . . . I only eat when I absolutely have to (but I don't binge) and then purge whatever I do eat . . . '
Victims suffering anorexia do not always completely restrict. Often at times when they cannot avoid a meal or food they will follow any consumption with self-induced vomiting or laxative abuse. This is considered 'anorexia, purging type'.

'I am above/on the high end of my healthy weight range . . . I cannot possibly have an eating disorder . . . '
Victims suffering any eating disorder can be of any weight. For most victims weight will continuously be going up and down. The weight of a person's body does not indicate their overall health, nor does it change the danger each victim may be in! There are more dangers involved in the

disordered eating patterns themselves, rather than in each victim's actual weight.

'I eat a lot of candy, and can't possibly be anorexic . . . '
Many anorexics and bulimics are junk-food addicts. There is little nutritional value to junk food but they serve as a false sense of energy. They also appease extreme cravings . . . for example, a victim's system may be depleted of sodium so there may be a strong craving for something salty. A bag of chips would seem to satisfy this craving. It is not uncommon to find a victim of anorexia or bulimia who lives solely on candy

(or junk food), and like any eating disorder victim, this puts them in great danger. Other common 'replacements' are drugs, alcohol, coffee, tea and/or cigarettes.

'Only middle-class, white teenagers suffer . . . '
ANYONE can suffer from anorexia or bulimia. Regardless of previously held beliefs, it is not only young, middle-class white teenagers or college students who can suffer. African-American, Hispanic, Asian, or white, women or men, rich to poor, from their teen years well into their fifties, there are victims from every age-bracket, class and culture.

Don't rely on the 'written statistics' – they are based on reports made to government agencies and if a country, state, or province doesn't require that doctors report the cases, the statistics will not be accurate. Keep in mind as well, the more shame a victim feels, the less likely that they will come forward and say they have an eating disorder . . . so if we keep perpetuating the idea that only 'young white women' suffer, less and less victims that don't fit this ideal will come forward, be acknowledged, and get the help they deserve.

'I eat three meals a day (or I eat a lot during the course of a day) and never purge. How can I have an eating disorder?'

Disordered eating doesn't always mean restricting, bingeing and/or purging. Victims sometimes eat 3 meals a day, or eat continuously throughout the day and through this can deceive themselves into thinking that all is fine. If these eating patterns or meals consist of only lettuce, salad or yoghurt (or other comparably low calorie, low fat food), and the calorie intake overall is far below normal (and is combined with emotional attributes), this would be considered anorexia. A victim may not be 'starving' themselves of food *per se*, but of any real calories, substance and nutrition. (The same is illustrated above in the example of eating candy.)

'I don't make myself vomit or use laxatives, I cannot be bulimic . . .'

There are other methods of 'purging' following a binge. The person suffering with bulimia will eat an unusually large quantity of food in a short period of time and follow it with purging. In addition to using laxatives or inducing vomiting, purging can also be compulsive exercise or complete fasting. This is one of the attributes that can be present in a person suffering both anorexia (restriction and purging without bingeing) and bulimia (bingeing and purging).

'My family member/friend eats normally around me. He/She can't possible have an eating disorder . . .'

It is not uncommon for victims of anorexia, bulimia and compulsive eating to eat 'normally' around others. This type of victim may look forward to their time alone, to be able to 'make up for' the time they've spent eating 'normally' around others. Anorexics will completely starve themselves, bulimics will binge and purge, and compulsive overeaters will overeat or binge once they have got back into their solitary environment. Victims may even look forward to being alone so they can partake in disordered eating patterns.

'This is just a phase . . .'

Anorexia, bulimia and compulsive overeating are not phases a child, teen or adult goes through. Some may go through dieting phases but this is far different from having an eating disorder.

'I take vitamin/mineral supplements so I know I will stay healthy . . .'

Vitamin supplements will not protect victims from the harm an eating disorder will expose the body to. Vitamins and minerals are absorbed into the body much more efficiently through their source food, and work in harmony with one another to ensure the highest level of effectiveness and absorption. While taking vitamins and minerals may help to provide a sense of security, or even prolong certain aspects of health (like warding off infection), they will not protect you from the dangers associated with having an eating disorder, such as: the bowel or kidneys shutting down, shrinkage of the brain, dehydration, diabetes, TMJ Syndrome and misalignment of the teeth, tears in the oesophagus, ulcers, joint pain and arthritis, digestive and absorption problems, acid reflux disorders, cancer of the mouth and throat, low or high blood pressure, heart arrhythmia and cardiac arrest, loss of menstrual cycle, infertility, dilation of the intestines, or depression and suicide.

'Everyone who is overweight or fat has compulsive overeating . . .'

What defines the illnesses of compulsive overeating or binge eating disorder is more than just the weight range of the individual. Emotional eating, eating to fill a void, stuffing down feelings with bingeing, isolation and pushing others away are just some of the traits. There are also victims who suffer from compulsive overeating or binge eating disorder who are not extremely overweight, as well, there are other reasons an individual can be overweight (including medical reasons or genetic predispositions to a larger body size). The overall symptoms that help determine if a person suffers from any disordered eating are how their eating relates to a lack of self-esteem and ability to cope with pain, anger and stress.

'I can't die from this . . .'

Anorexia, bulimia and compulsive overeating kill their victims. Eating disorders have the highest rate of death out of any other psychological illness. Up to 30% of the victims of eating disorders (and maybe higher) will die as a result of a complication caused by the illness.

• The above information is an extract from the Something Fishy Web site on eating disorders which can be found at www.something-fishy.org

Victims suffering any eating disorder can be of any weight. For most victims weight will continuously be going up and down

Warning signs

Information from ANRED – Anorexia Nervosa and Related Eating Disorders, Inc.

Because everyone today seems concerned about weight, and because most people diet at least once in a while, it is hard to tell what is normal behaviour and what is a problem that may escalate to threaten life and happiness. No one person will show all of the characteristics listed below, but people with eating disorders will manifest several.

In addition, the early stages of an eating disorder can be difficult to define. When does normative dieting become a health and emotional problem? When does weight loss cross the line and become pathological? Answering these questions is hard, especially when the person has not yet lost enough weight to qualify for a clinical diagnosis. Nevertheless, the questions are important. The sooner an eating disorder is treated, the easier it will be for the person to recover. If warning signs and symptoms are allowed to persist until they become entrenched behaviours, the person may struggle for years before s/he can turn matters around.

Food behaviours

The person skips meals, takes only tiny portions, will not eat in front of other people, eats in ritualistic ways, and mixes strange food combinations. May chew mouthfuls of food but spit them out before swallowing. Grocery shops and cooks for the entire household, but will not eat the tasty meals. Always has an excuse not to eat: is not hungry, just ate with a friend, is feeling ill, is upset, and so forth.

Becomes 'disgusted' with former favourite foods like red meat and desserts. Will eat only a few 'safe' foods. Boasts about how healthy the meals s/he does consume are. Becomes a 'vegetarian' but will not eat the necessary fats, oils, whole grains, and the denser fruits and veggies (such as sweet potatoes and avocados) required by true vegetarianism. Chooses primarily low-fat items with low levels of other nutrients, foods such as lettuce, tomatoes, sprouts, and so forth.

Always has a diet soda in hand. Drastically reduces or completely eliminates fat intake. Reads food labels religiously. If s/he breaks self-imposed rigid discipline and eats normal or large portions, excuses self from the table to vomit and get rid of the calories.

Or, in contrast to the above, the person gorges, usually in secret, and empties cupboards and refrigerator. May also buy special binge food. If panicked about weight gain, may purge to get rid of the calories. May leave clues that suggest discovery is desired: empty boxes, cans, and food packages; foul smelling bathrooms; running water to cover sounds of vomiting; excessive use of mouthwash and breath mints; and in some cases, containers of vomit poorly hidden that invite discovery.

Sometimes the person uses laxatives, diet pills, water pills, or 'natural' products from health food stores to promote weight loss. May abuse alcohol or street drugs, sometimes to deaden appetite, sometimes to escape emotional pain, and usually in hope of feeling better, at least temporarily.

Appearance and body image behaviours

The person loses, or tries to lose, weight. Has frantic fears of weight gain and obesity. Wears baggy clothes, sometimes in layers, to hide fat, hide emaciation, and stay warm. Obsesses about clothing size. Complains that s/he is fat even though others truthfully say this is not so. S/he will not believe them.

Spends lots of time inspecting self in the mirror and usually finds something to criticise. Detests all or specific parts of the body, especially breasts, belly, thighs, and buttocks. Insists s/he cannot feel good about self unless s/he is thin, and s/he is never thin enough to satisfy her/himself

Exercise behaviours

The person exercises excessively and compulsively. May tire easily, keeping up a harsh regimen only through sheer will power. As time passes, athletic performance suffers. Even so, s/he refuses to change the routine.

May develop strange eating patterns, supposedly to enhance athletic performance. May consume sports drinks and supplements, but total calories are less than what an active lifestyle requires.

Thoughts

In spite of average or above-average intelligence, the person thinks in magical and simplistic ways, for example, 'If I am thinner, I will feel better about myself.' S/he loses the ability to think logically, evaluate reality objectively, and admit and correct undesirable consequences of choices and actions.

Becomes irrational, argues with people who try to help, and then withdraws, sulks, or throws a tantrum. Wanting to be special, s/he becomes competitive. Strives to be the best, the smallest, the thinnest, and so forth.

Has trouble concentrating. Obsesses about food and weight and holds to rigid, perfectionistic standards for self and others.

Feelings

Has trouble talking about feelings, especially anger. Denies anger, saying something like, 'Everything is OK. I am just tired and stressed.' Escapes stress by turning to binge food, exercise, or anorexic rituals.

Becomes moody, irritable, cross, snappish, and touchy. Responds to confrontation and even low-intensity interactions with tears, tantrums, or withdrawal. Feels s/he does not fit in and therefore avoids friends and activities. Withdraws into self and feelings, becoming socially isolated.

Social behaviours

Tries to please everyone and withdraws when this is not possible. Tries to take care of others when s/he is the person who needs care. May present self as needy and dependent or conversely as fiercely independent and rejecting of all attempts to help. Anorexics tend to avoid sexual activity. Bulimics may engage in casual or even promiscuous sex.

Person tries to control what and where the family eats. To the dismay of others, s/he consistently selects low-fat, low-sugar non-threatening – and unappealing – foods and restaurants that in the past have provided these 'safe' items.

Relationships tend to be either superficial or dependent. Person craves true intimacy but at the same time is terrified of it. As in all other areas of life, anorexics tend to be rigidly controlling while bulimics have problems with lack of impulse control that can lead to rash and regrettable decisions about sex, money, stealing, commitments, careers, and all forms of social risk taking.

Please note: ANRED information is not a substitute for medical treatment or psychological care. For help with the physical and emotional problems associated with eating and exercise disorders, talk to your physician and a competent mental health professional.

• The above information is an extract from the ANRED – Anorexia Nervosa and Related Eating Disorders, Inc. web site which can be found at www.anred.com

© ANRED Anorexia Nervosa and Related Eating Disorders, Inc.

Helping a friend or relative

Information from the Eating Disorders Association (EDA)

'My friend keeps skipping meals. She won't eat in front of others.'

'My cousin only talks about food, or the shape of her body. She is very critical of herself.'

'My friend only thinks about her weight and body shape.'

'My brother tries to be perfect in every way. He worries all the time about what other people think of him.'

'My friend sometimes starts eating, and just can't stop.'

'My sister has become very distant from us. She seems to keep herself away from her family and friends.'

'My friend keeps disappearing into the toilet. I don't think she even knows she has a problem.'

Do any of these thoughts seem familiar to you? Do you think that a friend of yours, or someone in your family, has an eating disorder?

Some of the above signs might mean that someone has an eating

Eating Disorders Association

disorder. People with an eating problem may eat too much, or refuse to eat, because they feel unhappy. This can lead to emotional and physical problems.

If someone close to you has an eating disorder, you can be a great support in helping them cope with the illness. EDA's experience shows that friends and family can

really help people to recover. However, it's important for anyone with an eating problem to get medical advice. This gives their doctor the chance to make a proper diagnosis, and make sure they receive the right kind of help.

How you can help
What can you do if you think your friend or relative has an eating disorder?

You can really help by just being their friend, even when you feel your friendship is being rejected.

What can I do to help my friend?

Give time – and listen. Your friend may just need you to be there when things are hard to cope with. Listen to what they are saying. Try not to give advice, but encourage them to seek help. You should not take responsibility for their illness.

What if they don't accept there's a problem?

You may need to accept that your friend is not ready to tackle their eating disorder. But let them know how you are feeling. Tell them that they can come back to you later. Get some information about eating problems so you can help when your friend is ready to accept that there is a problem.

Should I change my eating habits to fit in with my friend?

No! Don't change your own eating habits. Unless your friend sees a 'normal' amount of food, they could get more and more out of touch with normality. Don't let your friend make you feel guilty about eating a healthy, balanced diet. Try not to talk about food or calories.

How can I stop worrying about my friend?

Don't let the illness ruin your life. Try to enjoy your usual activities, with or without your friend. You can talk in confidence to the Eating Disorders Association Youth Helpline if you want some support. Look after your own needs.

Should I encourage my friend to eat?

No. Everyone needs to decide for themselves what to eat. Your friend is responsible for their own needs.

Why don't they join in like they used to?

If your friend has an eating disorder they may find it increasingly hard to join in with social events. They may want to spend more time on their own, and may become more withdrawn and isolated. Tell them why you like them and that you value their friendship. Try to include them in activities. Even if they do not join in, they will still like to be asked. It will make them feel valued as a person, and help with their self-esteem.

Should I tell their parents?

If you find it too difficult to keep it secret, or feel concerned about your friend's safety, then tell an adult you trust. Tell your friend's parents if you really feel they should know. But let your friend know first that you are

going to tell someone. You may have to face the fact that they may not like what you have done, even if you did it for the best, but in time they will probably appreciate your decision.

Will it help if I cover up for my friend?

The best way to help is to let your friend take responsibility for their own behaviour. The problem may go on longer if you cover it up. It would be helpful though to suggest that your friend gets professional help. For instance, they could call the Eating Disorders Association Youth Helpline or arrange to see their doctor.

Treatment

The sooner the eating disorder is recognised and help given, the better the prognosis. Delay in recognition and treatment can result in the condition becoming more severe and needing more intensive treatment. Anorexia has one of the highest death rates of all psychiatric illnesses; research shows that deaths can be prevented by appropriate treatment. People with eating disorders are often afraid of asking for help and ambivalent about accepting it.

Outcome studies have shown that there is no one form of treatment which works for all patients; what is an effective form of treatment for one person may not be effective for another. Measuring 'recovery' is complex; users' views must be taken into account.

Family doctor

People with eating disorders cannot gain access to existing services without the condition being recognised and diagnosed. It may be difficult for GPs to recognise the disorder because:

- the patient is ashamed of the disorder, is reluctant to admit the problem, tries to disguise the condition and is therefore not forthcoming about the most important symptoms
- the patient is frightened of the consequences of admitting to having an eating disorder
- the doctor has little training or understanding of eating disorders.

All patients are entitled to complete confidentiality; this means that parents and carers are not entitled to confidential information. When patients are worried about confidentiality, agreement should be reached between them and the professional about what is to be written in their notes.

A few practices may have the expertise to take an active role in the treatment and monitoring of patients with eating disorders. In all other cases people diagnosed as having anorexia or bulimia nervosa should be referred for assessment by a professional who has training in eating disorders; a person referred for assessment should be seen as soon as possible; delays and waiting lists should be avoided since further deterioration may result in the need for in-patient rather than out-patient treatment.

General treatment

Effective treatment depends on the commitment of the patient to get better and the skills of the therapist. Effective types of treatment include: counselling, psychotherapy, cognitive behaviour therapy, group therapy, family therapy, day hospital programmes, in-patient treatment, dietetic advice, in some instances drugs can be of help in the short term.

Treatment must address the psychological aspects of anorexia and bulimia nervosa as well as the eating behaviour. Re-feeding alone may be successful in short-term weight restoration but is usually not effective in the long term.

Counselling

Counselling can be a very effective treatment if the counsellor has an understanding of anorexia and bulimia and is available long term. For anorexia, counselling is more effective during the early stages (when less than 25% of body weight has been lost). It is important that the doctor takes responsibility for medical monitoring of the person with an eating disorder.

Research shows that cognitive behaviour therapy is especially effective for people with bulimia.

Specialist treatment

Effective help is best provided by staff who understand eating disorders. People with eating disorders find that being treated by someone who does not understand the condition is ineffective and may make the condition worse. Specialist treatment may be available through local mental health service, general psychiatric hospitals or specialist units.

People with eating disorders should be involved as much as possible in their treatment programmes or care plans: e.g. patients should be able to see their case notes, patients should be involved in setting target weights, therapy should not be conditional on weight gain, vegetarian menus and appropriate food for minority groups should be available. Treatment should focus on emotional and psychological issues as well as weight.

The treatment package should include:

- education regarding the consequences of eating disorders
- counselling or psychotherapy
- monitoring of diet, weight and medical effects
- support and information for relatives and carers.

People with eating disorders need the continuity of a therapist who has time to build up trust, often over several years: e.g. an out-patient session of 10-15 minutes every month may be enough.

In-patient treatment should provide:

- a quiet and safe environment
- continuity of care from staff with an understanding of eating disorders
- staffing levels that enable support to be given during and after meals
- expert nutritional management and appropriate food
- ongoing counselling or psychotherapy

Follow-up and support after in-patient care is vital or the money and effort spent is wasted.

Some severely underweight people with anorexia nervosa can be treated successfully as day patients rather than in-patients.

If specialist treatment is not available locally, people with eating disorders should be referred through flexible contract arrangements or extra contractual referrals to NHS or private specialist centres.

Compulsory admission

In extreme circumstances and when all other alternatives have failed, people may be detained under the Mental Health Act in order to save life or reduce risk. In a survey of patients' views, of those people who had been admitted or detained against their wishes, 50% said that, in retrospect, they thought it had been a 'good thing'.

Minority groups

People from minority ethnic groups may have special needs; interpreters and advocates must be available to help the families.

Self-help

Self-help manuals may be useful as the first phase of treatment or alongside existing treatments. Self-help groups can be a useful adjunct to treatment but they are not an alternative; they help patients and families understand they are not alone with the illness. A self-help programme for women with bulimia is available through the Eating Disorders Association (under the medical supervision of a GP).

Carers

Effective treatment often involves working with families, carers and friends. The impact on the family of someone with an eating disorder can be enormous; families may also need support for themselves. Families need advice on what they should and should not do to contribute to an individual's recovery.

Feedback from patients

All units should have a clear and open complaints procedure; patients should be encouraged to give their views in a constructive way. Chief Executives of NHS Trusts need 'to make sure that the views of patients and relatives are included in the overall assessment of service quality'.

- For help with eating disorders including anorexia and bulimia nervosa contact:
Eating Disorders Association, First Floor Wensum House, 103 Prince of Wales Road, Norwich, NR1 1DW. Tel: 01603 621 414 (helpline – open 9.00am to 6.30pm weekdays) 01603 765 050 (youthline callers 18 & under – open 4.00pm to 6.00pm weekdays). E-mail: info@edauk.com Web site: www.edauk.com

© *Eating Disorders Association (EDA)*

The best way to help is to let your friend take responsibility for their own behaviour. The problem may go on longer if you cover it up

---

Body image in our time

From a feminist perspective. By Deanne Jade.

Body image is the subjective sense we have of our appearance and our body. Unlike what others see when they look at us, our body image is often different from the objective size and shape of our body. Both men and women sometimes feel dissatisfied with their body and its parts. Who hasn't met the man who would not like larger biceps or the woman who would not like longer legs? However more women than men report consistently disliking their bodies. The emphasis on women's experience isn't meant to imply that body image problems among men are less important than among women – simply less prevalent

Consider the following: by the age of 10, most girls are afraid of becoming fat. Many more adolescent schoolgirls than boys diet. Among college students a larger percentage of women than men report feeling unhappy about their looks. Women in the general population report more negative attitudes about their physical appearance than do men. Sadly, negative body image often begins when girls are young and extends far into adulthood. For some women it lasts their entire lives

Obsessive concern about body shape and weight has become so common among western women of all ages that it is now the norm. Moreover, results of a large survey indicate that body image problems are more common in the USA than in any other nation. When British women are asked what they want to change about their body they respond without hesitation, when asked what they like about their body their response requires considerably more thought.

Weight as a measure of self-worth

In our society, the 'thin is beautiful and beautiful is good' belief prevails. Consequently women often use weight as a yardstick with which to measure self-worth and attractiveness. It is common for women to enter a room and immediately determine their status by assessing which women are thinner and which are fatter than they are. As a result, being female often means feeling fat and inadequate.

A feminist understanding of negative body image views socio-cultural issues as the underpinning for body loathing among women. For example girls are socialised more than boys to focus on external aspects of themselves, such as their appearance. Learning to do their hair, polish their nails and paint their faces is virtually a rite of passage into womanhood in our culture. Boys, on the other hand, are typically socialised to concentrate on their athletic abilities rather than their looks. In addition attractiveness is not the prerequisite for masculinity as it is for femininity in our culture. Attractive men are described as handsome. 'Handsome' is derived from the middle English word 'handsom' which refers to the ability to manipulate or do. It is first a word about action and only secondarily about appearance. Associated with 'handsome' are qualities of achievement and strength. How often do you associate these attributes with 'beautiful' or 'pretty'?

Women are expected to have far more control over the body, its function, shape and size, than men. Open discussion and public displays of natural body functions such as sweating, belching and scratching are not as acceptable for women as they are for men. These functions are not only viewed as unfeminine but as evidence of masculinity.

How are body image problems manifested?

There are three basic aspects to negative body image: feelings/thoughts, behaviours and size perception

Example of negative body image thoughts include:
'I am fat and disgusting.'
'My thighs are so big I can't wear a bathing suit.'
'I look so fat next to Jane I can't go out with her.'
'Everyone notices my flat chest.'

Negative body thoughts can dramatically affect behaviour, relationships and self-esteem. Sometimes women develop bizarre eating habits, eat a restrictive and nutritionally deficient diet, and/or exercise excessively because of their desire to be thinner. The effect of negative body image on size perception is clearly evident in some women's tendency to over- or underestimate the size of their disliked body parts – even in the face of objective data indicating their error.

Interestingly, research has shown that men who exercise regularly are more likely to do so to build body mass and improve cardiovascular fitness. Women, on the other hand, are more likely to exercise to lose weight and change their shape in an effort to increase their attractiveness. Unhappily, this implies that exercise will lose its enjoyable quality for many women as it has become yet another way to manipulate their bodies.

Why is negative body image a problem?

The inordinate emphasis on women's external selves makes it very difficult for women to appreciate their internal selves. When women are so focused on their body, they are not able to devote much energy to other aspects of their lives.

Attempts to meet the ideal are often ineffective in the long run and can lead to physical, psychological and behavioural problems, including binge eating, obsessions about food and eating disorders. Other psychological effects of the pursuit of perfect body include low self-esteem, feelings of failure and inferiority, irritability, loss of libido and memory problems. Body dissatisfaction is also associated with depression, anxiety, relationship problems, self-contempt, and social introversion. Women pay a high price for being at war with their bodies.

Most women cannot physio-logically or psychologically attain the ideal; yet, for failing to do the impossible, they are viewed as irresponsible. The belief is that if only they worked hard enough at

---

Women are expected to have far more control over the body, its function, shape and size, than men

---

dieting, they would be thinner and more attractive. This is a myth. Only a small minority of women are genetically designed to naturally fall within the narrow weight range culturally ideal. When women deprive themselves to lose weight, their body retaliates by slowing its metabolism. This makes it more difficult to lose weight and intensifies the problem it was designed to remedy. Some researchers believe that repeated dieting attempts means dieters have to work harder each time they diet, increasing the likelihood of failure.

Although body image problems play a central role in dieting and in the development and maintenance of eating disorders, they also warrant treatment in their own sake. Research with non eating disordered college women indicates that many women want treatment simply for negative body image. This suggests the discomfort of negative body image, even at sub-clinical levels, is sufficient to interfere with quality of life. The sad part of this is that pressures against body acceptance are so great that women feel incapable of changing without help.

What role does the media play?

We must admit that what we know about cultural standards comes from the media. TV shows, movies, commercials, ads in newspapers, magazines – even on the backs of buses show us what is beautiful, good, and desirable. Young girls watching *Beverly Hills 90210* learn quickly that fat, pimply girls don't live in Beverly Hills, and if they do, they certainly don't get the guy.

The media presents a thinner than average woman as ideal, and implies a strong connection between

being thin, using beauty products, and being happy. In both entertainment and advertising, thinness is typically associated with status, wealth and success for women. Although there is no evidence that happiness is directly related to weight, that is the message continually pounded home. And females learn that lesson well.

Unrealistic and changing body standards breed a society of women who cannot accept their bodies as they are. Even if they are within a healthy weight range.

Powerful as the media's 'thin is good' message is, it is unfair to exclusively blame the media for women's body image ills. Advertisers and entertainment decision-makers build their empires on prevailing tastes and historical/cultural norms. If fat sold 'cokes', you can bet the 'ahah' girls would have been a size 40! The media plays on our likes and dislikes. Unfortunately, it also has the widespread reach that enables it to perpetuate and exacerbate biases and beliefs. The media is not responsible for the body dissatisfaction epidemic but is an integral part of it.

Are thin women happier than other women?

No. Many women believe that if they were thinner they would be happier. Research has clearly demonstrated that women who meet the body/ beauty ideal are just as likely to be unhappy about their looks as women who do not.

Interestingly, recent research with women who have had a mastectomy for breast cancer suggests they feel more satisfaction with the body than women who have not had breast surgery or disease. Despite not meeting the societal ideal, the women with the mastectomy report they become more appreciative of their body and less likely to treat it as an object to manipulate into a particular shape.

There is also strong evidence from research that 'drive for thinness' recedes as women become older – reaching their forties and fifties. Although this may be reflected in women being kinder to themselves on the dieting front, we do not yet know whether this is replaced by concerns and behaviour designed to reduce the effects of ageing.

Why do women try to meet the ideal?

Historically, attractiveness has been the only bargaining power women have had to access resources controlled by men. This has led to women competing with each other to meet the beauty ideal and reap the associated benefits. Despite the advances made by the Women's Movement, appearance remains intertwined with their identity, social success, economic pursuits and accomplishments. This stands in contrast to men, whose self-image is based more on their activities and accomplishments. Some feminists believe the association between women and appearance allows society to continue its male-dominated structure and prevents women from becoming too powerful.

Conclusion

Feeling at home in our bodies is essential to our well-being. As women examine the source of their body image dissatisfaction, they may view the discontent less as individual pathology and more as part of a larger system that oppresses women.

Eliminating beauty and body standards is unrealistic. However, a more diverse view of beauty is necessary to save women from additional physical and psychological tolls. To be productive, happy members of society, women must be well nourished and have energy to channel to other pursuits. This is not possible if they are obsessively counting calories, restricting their intake, daydreaming about food and weight, and futilely whipping their bodies into an unattainable shape. It is essential for women to consider the effects that the pursuit of the perfect body has on their lives and to challenge their beliefs about weight and appearance. With awareness of the cultural context and socio-cultural issues, and with the aid of additional strategies aimed at thinking and behaving differently, women can enhance their relationship with their body. This will allow women to live life more fully and meaningfully.

• The above information is from the National Centre For Eating Disorders. See page 41 for address details.

Eating disorders, body image and the media

Overview of a report by the British Medical Association

Introduction

This report considers the role that the media can play in shaping young people's attitudes to eating and body shape, and developing self-esteem in the young who are at the greatest risk of developing an eating disorder. The report considers whether the media play a significant role in the causation of eating disorders, where they can 'trigger' the illness in vulnerable individuals, by suggesting that being 'thin' means being successful, and how they affect young people who may have low self-esteem or unhealthy attitudes towards food. More positively, the media may be able to significantly contribute towards developing high self-esteem in young people, and actively participate in health promotion to combat the mistaken belief that 'thin = healthy' and that 'dieting', rather than healthy eating and regular exercise, is the way to achieve a healthy weight.

General summary

- Eating disorders are a significant cause of mortality and morbidity in young people, particularly young women. Even if young people recover from an eating disorder, they may suffer long-term health problems as a result of their illness.
- Eating disorders are caused by a complex interplay between genetics, family history and the cultural environment.
- Social factors implicated in the development of eating disorders include sociocultural norms regarding thinness, eating, food preparation and roles of women.
- The media provide particular examples of role expectations and images of beauty which may influence young people's perceptions of acceptable body image.
- Obesity is an increasing problem in the UK, with adverse consequences for health. However, the considerable health risks for women associated with being underweight are less well publicised.
- Dieting is an important precipitant factor in the development of eating disorders. Young women are dieting at an increasingly young age, and expressing dissatisfaction with their body shapes.
- Many young people do not eat regular family meals and may not have positive associations with food. This may place them at risk of developing an eating disorder.
- Eating disorders became more prevalent in Western industrialised countries in the latter part of the 20th century.
- Fewer Asian and black women apparently suffer from eating disorders, although there are higher rates amongst immigrants to Western society and ethnic minority populations raised in

Western industrialised cultures, or those following a Western model of development.

- Eating disorders predominantly affect young women. However, evidence from studies of men with eating disorders also suggest that perceived body image measured against a societal 'norm' is a crucial factor in the onset of the illness.

- Although certain biological predispositions (which may in part be genetically determined) may contribute to the onset of eating disorders in an individual, historical and cross-cultural evidence suggests that the development of eating disorders is significantly influenced by particular aspects of modern society.

- The media are a significant and pervasive influence in modern society, and provide information about gender roles, fashion and acceptable body image which may be particularly influential on those young children and adolescents who are heavily exposed to its content.

- Advertising, in particular, may influence young people's perception of fashion, beauty and attitudes towards food.

- Young women may compare themselves to extremely thin models, working in the fashion industry or advertising products, and perceive themselves as 'fat' in comparison, rather than healthy and attractive.

- For eating disorder sufferers, their bodies become the means by which they judge the success of their lives. Encouraging and developing self-esteem which is not dependent upon body size may be a key to protecting vulnerable individuals from developing eating disorders.

- The media can boost self-esteem where it is providing examples of a variety of body shapes, roles and routes of achievement for young men and women. However, it often tends to portray a limited number of body shapes and messages linking external appearance with success — this is potentially damaging to the self-esteem of young people.

- The media are an important source of health care information for young people, particularly through the medium of women's magazines, and their positive contribution to health should not be underestimated. However, it is important that care and consideration are given to the messages that are conveyed by the media and received by young people.

- Primary prevention programmes for eating disorders aim to reduce risk factors for the illness and increase young people's resistance to risk factors. Changes can be made at a societal level to achieve these goals, for example, reducing exposure to media images of thin women and increasing awareness of issues relating to body image, self-esteem and pressure to diet, in the school curriculum.

Recommendations

The media

1. Broadcasters (or programme makers) and magazine publishers should adopt a more responsible editorial attitude towards the depiction of extremely thin women

as role models, and should portray a more realistic range of body images.

2. Producers of TV and printed advertisements should consider more carefully their use of thin women to advertise products, in particular the ITC should review its policy on the use of thin models to advertise products other than slimming aids.

3. Health professionals should work with the television industry to increase awareness of the possible impact of programming on young people, and encourage the inclusion of healthy eating patterns into their programming.

Diet and nutrition

4. Health professionals should work with food manufacturers and advertising agencies to increase awareness of the key nutritional issues that affect young people. In particular there should be increased awareness of the impact of faulty nutrition in young adolescents going through puberty.

5. The school curriculum should include the development of critical viewing skills in order to interpret food advertising. Consideration should be given to implementing media literacy programmes, particularly for young children.

6. Health care workers who work directly with children and teenagers must ensure that dieting is not part of a routine unless it is absolutely necessary; it is crucially important that being put on a 'diet' is clearly distinguished from 'dieting' – i.e. food restriction. Clear, achievable and biologically appropriate targets should be set by health care professionals if dieting is considered necessary.

Education

7. Schools should have clearly defined anti-bullying policies, and strongly discourage the teasing of overweight children. This should encourage a greater acceptance of normal variation in body size and shape within the population.

8. Schools should develop policies on eating disorders, to enable early detection of the signs and symptoms in children, which could be related to anorexia or bulimia nervosa.

9. School counselling and mentoring services should provide an arena in which young people can address issues of self-esteem, body shape and social popularity.

10. Consideration should be given to the problems faced by young people during physical education classes, e.g. self-consciousness about body shape, fearing being 'picked last' in a team due to perceived physical unsuitability. Fitness and enjoyment should be considered the key priorities, and children of all body shapes and sizes should be made to feel included in lessons and valued for their contributions, even if they are unable to achieve high levels of success.

Government health strategy

11. The Government's mental health strategy as set out in *Our Healthier Nation* should set clearly defined targets for the reduction in the number of eating disorders, by consideration of preventive measures.

12. There should be increased public education on the connections between dieting, physical activity and health, and health risks associated with eating disorders and being underweight.

13. More resources should be given for mental health services, specifically eating disorder clinics.

Further research

14. The greatest research priority should be given to trials of primary prevention for eating disorders, especially among children and adolescents. These trials should include the provision of a control group, full assessment, optimum follow-up after a reasonable time-lag, with miminum drop-out rates.

15. There should be more research into the subject of the media and possible related effects on children and adolescents, particularly the impact on perceptions of body shape and healthy eating.

16. There should be more research into the 'protective' factors which seem to result in greatly reduced incidence of eating disorders in certain sectors of the population (e.g. men, certain ethnic minorities).

- *Eating Disorders, Body Image and the Media* is available from the: BMJ Bookshop, Burton Street, London, WC1H 9JR. Tel: 020 7383 6244. Fax: 020 7383 6455. E-mail: orders@bmjbookshop.com Price: £7.95. ISBN: 0 7279 15339

© British Medical Association (BMA)

Body image and eating disorders

Information from the British Nutrition Foundation (BNF)

The government has asked the broadcasting standards commission to evaluate whether a sufficiently diverse group of women appear as presenters and guests on television. The monitoring is designed to address growing concerns that images of excessively thin models in magazines and on television have led to an increase in eating disorders.

A recent study on body image, eating disorders and the media by the British Medical Association found that many models and actresses, who are commonly cited as popular role models by young girls, have 10-15% of their body composition as fat whereas the average proportion of body fat for a healthy woman is between 22-26%.

A recent government survey reporting on the diets of British schoolchildren found that one in six girls aged 15-18 years were dieting to lose weight. The survey also found that this age group was most likely to

BRITISH
Nutrition
FOUNDATION

have poor intakes of a number of vitamins and minerals, including vitamin D, iron, calcium and zinc.

Anorexia and bulimia nervosa are debilitating diseases, which can be fatal. In most cases the disease results in a poor nutritional status that can increase the risk of secondary diseases such as osteoporosis and heart disease. The treatment of these conditions requires a multi-disciplinary approach as the causative factors are extremely complex.

Anorexia and bulimia can be triggered by a life event. Sufferers use excessive slimming and exercising as a way of controlling certain aspects of their lives, at a time when they feel unable to control other events.

It must also be recognised that obesity and overweight are increasing rapidly in the UK population. Being obese and overweight is associated with increased risk of heart disease, cancer, stroke and diabetes mellitus; these are currently the leading causes of death in Britain. While it is prudent to be aware of the pressures that images of extremely thin women can have on vulnerable young girls, it is also crucial that support and education are provided for those who are overweight and wish to achieve a healthy body weight.

- The above information is an extract from the British Nutrition Foundation's web site which can be found at www.nutrition.org.uk Alternatively, see page 41 for their address details.

© British Nutrition Foundation 2000

Thin stars on TV 'put pressure on the young'

By Sandra Barwick

The abnormal thinness of women on television and in magazines may be putting so much pressure on young women that it is contributing to eating disorders carrying a high death rate, the British Medical Association said yesterday.

The image of the female form being projected in the media was so unrealistic that it encouraged vulnerable young women to try for the impossible, it warned. But extreme skinniness – particularly as demonstrated by some fashion models – was 'both unachievable and biologically inappropriate', the association said in a new report.

A BMA spokesman said: 'Young girls try to emulate the very thin women they see on television and in adverts, and it's not possible without starving themselves. Even if they don't die they can cause themselves permanent, irreversible damage.'

Research has estimated that most fashion models and television actresses in the Nineties had 10 to 15 per cent body fat – as opposed to 22 to 26 per cent for a healthy woman. The gap between the media ideal and reality appears to be making eating disorders worse. A BMA report, *Eating Disorders, Body Image and the Media*, said: 'Models are becoming thinner at a time when women are becoming heavier, and the gap between the ideal body shape and the reality is wider than ever.'

The result is that women are pressurised, feeling their bodies are fat by comparison, and vulnerable adolescents are particularly susceptible. Low self-esteem is part of the reason for the development of eating disorders, which have complex causes.

The report says: 'At present certain sections of the media provide images of extremely thin or underweight women in contexts which suggest that these weights are healthy or desirable.' Normal women in the upper reaches of a healthy weight should be 'more in evidence on television as role models for young women', it recommends.

Models and actresses are often dress sizes 8 to 10: ordinary healthy women can range up to size 16. Half of adolescent girls are thought to read fashion and beauty-related magazines, and at the same time are at their peak exposure to television.

The report does not name any programmes or adverts, but television's Ally McBeal, played by Calista Flockhart, Liz Hurley, the face of Estée Lauder, and 'Posh Spice', Victoria Beckham, have, with many others, been criticised for their extreme thinness.

The death rate from eating disorders, which typically begin in young women, is one of the highest in all psychiatric illnesses, and the number of sufferers from eating disorders such as anorexia and bulimia nervosa is rising.

Chloe Cunningham, of Cunningham Management in west London, an agency representing television presenters, said that the report highlighted concerns she had had for a number of years. She said: 'I get terribly fed up with producers saying a client of mine is overweight, and being asked "Could she lose a few pounds?", when she's absolutely not. I think it's ridiculous. I'd rather lose the job than tell someone that.

'I'm a woman, and it's something I feel strongly about. It's getting to be a different race on television to normal life. It's disgraceful. Even people like Gaby Roslin and Carol Vorderman, who weren't fat, have

> ## The death rate from eating disorders is one of the highest in all psychiatric illnesses

felt the need to lose even more weight. Television has created a fake idea of what's normal. To look good on television you have to have an angular face, and some women in prominent jobs are getting so vain they want to look like a skull. In real life they look ill.'

Jade da Silva, 38, an actress from Camden, north London, who has recently arrived in Britain from Australia, said that there were very few roles for anyone her size, which would be seen as perfectly normal on the High Street. She said: 'I'm five foot seven inches and a dress size 16 – I'm not obese, but I am quite large, and I've had quite a few agents tell me I would have to lose weight before they would take me on.

'On auditions, people make up their minds before they've even seen you perform. You do have to be thin to be successful. You might be a better actress, but the leading role will always go to a skinny person.'

Around 60,000 in Britain are believed to suffer from eating disorders, the majority of whom are young women. Anorexia nervosa affects up to two per cent of females between 15 and 30. The report says that up to 20 per cent of these cases are likely to end in death.

Television producers and those in advertising should review their employment of very thin women, and the Independent Television Commission should review its advertising policy, the report recommends. Schools should work harder to prevent fat children from being bullied or teased and they should educate all children to be more critical of food advertisements.

The report calls for more research into the link between media images and eating disorders, and into the reasons why some groups appear to be resilient to them. Only one in 10 sufferers is male, and black women appear to be less susceptible to them.

Pressure to be thin affecting young women's self-esteem

Body image summit

Many young women are being held back from fulfilling their aspirations and reaching their potential because they lack confidence and self-esteem, Tessa Jowell, Minister for Women, is expected to warn today at the Body Image Summit.

Speaking at the summit, to take place at the Institute of Civil Engineers in Westminster with leading figures from the worlds of fashion, modelling and women's media, the Minister will say:

'Young women themselves, their mothers and grandmothers have all told us they want to see more women with a wider range of body shapes and sizes and more women from ethnic minorities as models in magazines.

'The pressure they feel to be thin can undermine self-esteem and confidence, which in turn can have an impact on their health and well-being.

'We are in the business of ensuring that every young woman can reach her full potential. We want the girls of this country to have opportunities and choices, in all aspects of their lives. We want them to achieve their aspirations to have good jobs, good pay and satisfying lives.'

However, Tessa Jowell will make it clear that the Government does not intend to regulate on this issue nor is it in the business of defining what the 'right' body shape should be:

'This summit is not about telling women, the fashion industry or the world of film and media what to do or how to do it. We are certainly not saying these industries are responsible for causing eating disorders amongst young girls. We recognise the important contribution these industries make to the economy.

'The summit is about stimula-

ting the debate and key people finding ways to address the concerns of young women. This isn't about regulation or restricting the freedom of any individual, any company or any industry.'

Yvette Cooper, Minister for Public Health, will add:

'The National Diet and Nutrition Survey we recently published showed that on average 6% of girls are on a diet. It also shows that by the time they reach 15-18 years, this has risen to 16%, compared to 3% of boys in the same age group. And it shows that on average girls are doing very little physical activity and eating less than half the recommended amount of fruit and vegetables.'

Other speakers at the summit will include Susie Orbach, psychotherapist, Liz Jones, editor of *Marie Claire* and three young women. Rebecca Martin, editor of teen magazine *Jump*, will also attend the summit.

A video will be shown at the summit illustrating the pressures that young women feel to be thin and to conform to the 'ideal' body shape. Three young women who appear in the video will also be addressing the meeting.

Girls, self-esteem and body image: key facts

- 57.5% of girls say their appearance is the biggest concern in their lives (Exeter University's Schools Health Education Department, 1998).
- Among girls aged 12 and 13, 59% cent of those with low self-esteem are watching their weight and on diets (Exeter University's Schools Health Education Department, 1998).
- Models and actresses in the media today generally have 10-15% body fat whereas the average body fat for a healthy women is 22-26% (*Eating Disorders, Body Image and the Media*, BMA, 2000).

- 61% of 18 to 24-year-old women said they feel inadequate compared to the media's image of beautiful women and only 25% of young women were happy with their weight (*Pressure to be Perfect*, Bread for Life Campaign, 1998).
- 91% felt it was bad that the media always portray so-called perfect women, 89% wanted more average-sized models used in magazines and 63% wanted fewer dieting features (*Pressure to be Perfect*, Bread for Life Campaign, 1998).
- Research suggests that a sudden increase in eating disorders among teenage girls in Fiji may be linked to the arrival of television in the mid 90s and 'Western ideals of beauty'. The study found that 75% of Fijian girls questioned reported feeling 'too big or fat' and 15% said that they had vomited to control their weight (Research by Harvard anthropologist Anne Becker, 1998).
- Eating disorders generally develop between the ages of 15 and 25 years (Eating Disorders Association).
- Estimates suggest that about one in a hundred young women has bulimia nervosa (Eating Disorders Association).
- Women with anorexia nervosa outnumber men by a ratio of 10:1 (Eating Disorders Association).
- 19% of 11-17-year-old young women in a recent survey were on diets with fairly high numbers dieting even among 11 and 12-year-olds (*Today's Girl, Tomorrow's Woman*, Guide Association, 2000).
- 88% of young women say that there is a lot of pressure from the media to 'look perfect' and 42% believe their life would be easier if they were more attractive (*Today's Girl, Tomorrow's Woman*, Guide Association, 2000).

© Cabinet Office

Society and eating disorders

By Colleen Thompson

It is not surprising that eating disorders are on the increase because of the value society places on being thin. Women are given the message at a very young age that in order to be happy and successful, they must be thin. Every time you walk into a store you are surrounded by the images of emaciated models that appear on the front cover of all fashion magazines. Thousands of teenage girls are starving themselves this very minute trying to attain what the fashion industry considers to be the 'ideal' figure. The average model weighs 23% less than the average woman. Maintaining a weight that is 15% below your expected body weight fits the criteria for anorexia, so most models, according to medical standards, fit into the category of being anorexic. Teenagers need to realise that society's ideal body image is not achievable. The photos we see in magazines are not real either. Many people don't realise that those photos have gone through many touch-ups and have been air-brushed to make the models look perfect. Teenagers striving to attain society's unattainable ideal image will just end up increasing their feelings of inadequacy.

Teenagers are under a lot of pressure to be thin. They are led to believe that the only way they can be accepted and fit in, is if they are thin. They resort to starving, vomiting and eating only diet foods to try and be thin. Television is a big influence on them. They watch shows like *Beverly Hills 90210* and *Melrose Place* and feel they need to look as thin as the actresses on these shows. Many actresses we see on TV have endured hours of exercise and have deprived themselves of the proper nutrition in order to maintain a thin figure. Some even resort to plastic surgery, liposuction and breast implants. You just have to watch an episode of *Baywatch* to know that statement is true. Society is brainwashing young people into believing that being thin is important and necessary.

Diet commercials are constantly appearing on our television screens telling us that once we lose the weight, we will be happy. While you're standing in the check-out line at the grocery store you are surrounded by magazines claiming to have the newest and best diet. Each month another new diet appears claiming to be the diet to end all diets. Whatever happened to last month's diets that claimed the same thing? Dieting has become an obsession. We spend billions of dollars each year trying to look the way society tells us we need to look. If diets really worked, then why are there so many of them? The reason a new diet pops up each month is because last's month's diets did not work. You know, the ones that claimed to really work. The truth of the matter is that **diets don't work**. As soon as you start to diet, you automatically set yourself up for failure. Many of the diets on the market right now are also unhealthy. They deprive you of the proper nutrition your body needs to survive and these diets can lead to health problems.

The diet and fashion industries are not totally to blame for society's obsession with thinness. We are the ones keeping them in business. We buy into the idea that we can attain the 'ideal' body image. We allow ourselves to believe the lies being thrown at us constantly. We buy their magazines, diet books and products, hoping that this time they will work. We are throwing away our hard-earned money trying to live up to the standards that society has set for us. Be prepared to spend lots of money on your quest for the perfect diet and be prepared to never find it, because there isn't one.

It's unfortunate, but in today's society, people have forgotten that it's what's inside a person that counts, not what's on the outside. We need to start loving and accepting each other for who we are, not what we look like. Next time you decide that you are going to start another diet because you feel you are too fat, stop, sign up for a self-esteem class instead. That would be money well spent. If we learn to love and accept ourselves, we will also begin to love our bodies, no matter what size we are.

We also need to teach our children to be proud of who they are. We need to remind them that people come in all shapes and sizes, and we need to teach them to accept everyone for who they are. Parents need to also teach their children the value of healthy eating and not send the message that being thin is important. Many children, under the age of 10, are becoming obsessed with dieting and their bodies. They are afraid of becoming fat. They don't just learn this from the media, they also learn this from their parents. If their mothers are constantly dieting and expressing their desire to be thin, these young children will start to believe they also need to be thin. We need to encourage and support our children, especially teenagers. They need to feel good about themselves and their accomplishments, they need your approval and

they need to know that you are proud of them. If a child is raised to love and accept who they are and what they look like, they will be less likely to strive to fit into society's unattainable standards.

Once again, I would like to stress the fact that diets don't work. Eating three healthy meals a day, a few snacks and doing moderate exercise, will allow your body to go to its natural set point. It's important to remember that no food will make you fat, as long as it's eaten in moderation. Stop buying those

fashion magazines and diet products, and stop believing all the lies being told to you by the fashion and diet industries. Instead, focus on learning to love and accept yourself. No number on a scale and fitting into a smaller dress size will not make you happy. Happiness can only come from within.

• The above information is an extract from the Mirror-Mirror web site which can be found at www.mirror-mirror.org/eatdis.htm

© Colleen Thompson

What you should know

Information from the National Centre For Eating Disorders

- Normal women overestimate body size – not just anorexics, as formerly believed.
- Persons who are underweight will always experience deep hunger until normal weight has been restored for a while. That is just the way it is.
- Fat people who lose weight will continue to experience themselves as fat. Fat women who have lost weight report feeling fat much more than women who were never overweight. This is like the 'missing limb' syndrome. They continue to retain a sense that their body is unacceptable. They

By Deanne Jade

focus on areas where less weight was lost. Stunkard reports that people who were overweight as children are more likely to experience this 'phantom fat'. They need to understand that this is normal.

- Persons overweight since childhood are likely to catastrophise if they regain just a few pounds after losing weight, and are less likely to have recovery strategies.
- Fat people who do not improve

in body image as they lose weight are more likely to drop out of weight loss programmes.
- Bulimics continue to have poor body image even after successful treatment; however other elements of self-esteem improve.

The magic ideal weight

What is it and what is the quality of longing for it? Where does it come from? Is it precise? What are the influences which conspire to set it – is it the past, the present, personal history? (Note the importance of having body problems in childhood like being too tall or having glasses and the effect of teasing.) Note also the influence of other people, friends or family.

Is the Magic Weight to do with Weight Watchers (note that the concept of a goal weight is faulty). A range is more realistic and the lower level is set by fat cell biology.

Research has shown that bulimia is associated with poor body image in the mother. Dieting in a mother is more likely to lead to dieting behaviour and weight dissatisfaction in daughters.

How people with serious body image problems will be in therapy

- Over restraint. Narrow range of foods. Address by broadening choices.
- Subtle dieting. Advise the client to give up dieting 'just for tomorrow' after that they can re-decide.

- Continual complaints about weight. If the client is bulimic and/or normal weight and desperate to lose, remind them that they may have to choose between being as they are and stable in their eating, or thinner and compulsive.
- 'I want to go on a diet' can be construed as a cry for help. What else is not working in their life? What things will not change if they are thinner? What would they be prepared to barter for an extra half stone less in weight?
- 'I feel fat!' Reframe if possible by asking them to identify exactly how they feel fat. Is it the feeling of their clothes, of the size of a particular part of their body, or is it the sight of someone else, or is it an internal experience like being bloated. It is often a trigger for bad eating – a sense of being a failure. What has triggered this

feeling? Could it be just knowing that something fattening has been eaten? Often women experience themselves as feeling fat when they are really suffering from a mild temporary depression. Feeling fat is a way of taking on the culture's ideas of what fatness represents such as laziness, greediness, lack of success, being unloved etc.

The important thing is to help people not react to fat feelings with their usual strategies (cutting back) or thought processes (beating oneself up). People sit back and wait peacefully for the feeling to pass – such as relaxation/doing something nice for oneself on a fat day/going for a gentle swim or walk etc. No point in sending someone out for an hour of aerobics.

It may help them to feel less tense but it doesn't do that much to calories.

© National Centre For Eating Disorders

Looking good

Information from Pupiline

Are you dressing to impress?
Well, if you are a female person of our society then of course you are, that's what girlies do!! But hang on a mo, do you buy the latest design of cropped trousers because they look good on Naomi Campbell or because they look good on you and you feel comfortable? To look good I believe you need to feel good as well, and you need to be yourself and be happy with who you are, however there is a growing problem that many young girls out there are trying too hard to be like their role models.

To find out more about models and how their looks can influence other young girls, read on.

Everyone likes to look good, why not, we can then feel good about ourselves, and we may even be lucky enough to attract someone of the opposite sex! The problems start when we look in the mirror and we see something that we don't want to see, yes I know a big red spot on your

---

By Natalie

---

forehead, no, it's when we are unhappy with the way we look. Many factors can be the trigger of these feelings

Catalogues
Picture this: you are looking through your catalogue in the hope of finding something sparkly and spangly to wear out next weekend for your best bud's birthday 'night out', you flip over the page and finally find

---

To look good I believe you need to feel good as well, and you need to be yourself and be happy with who you are'

---

something that you think you like, then you stop and look at the girl who's modelling your dress, how do you feel? Answer: Before you began looking at the catalogue you probably felt really excited and motivated towards buying something for your bud's night out, but when someone else is modelling your dress, it suddenly seems less appealing. Research has shown that girls' motivation levels can easily be destroyed by simply showing them pictures of models.

Big is beautiful
However, I think that if young girls were to see 'everyday' girlies modelling their clothes, like your average next-door neighbour, then people would feel more relaxed and comfortable. It is very off-putting to find that your newly bought black dress looks better on Victoria Beckham than it does on you. False images are a bad thing and I feel that we girlies are given false hopes, but don't worry girls it's simply

advertising to earn money and just imagine what poor old Posh Spice looks like when she gets up in the morning (it's a horrible thought!!) but no one looks great in the morning do they?

Eating the right kind of food

Eating is a way for our body to function, so we need to eat something, and we all know that we never eat healthily 100% of the time, but when we start to eat nothing at all we then need help.

Why do people turn to a no-food diet?

When we look at models they seem to have long white faces that look tired and unwell, their bodies are barely visible and they have no definite shape or structure. Is this the image that advertisers want to convey? Is this what we want young people to believe is the right way to be in order to look good and be successful?

This is wrong, everyone is who they are and who they want to be, and images like this encourage young girlies to feel that this is the right way. As a result the only way to look as good as the models (do they really look good?) is to eat nothing. This eating disorder is known as anorexia and it is a growing problem in many young girls. If you feel that you or anyone else needs help then please contact the Helpline number.

Images of models can be found everywhere that we look, and I think that these images need to be changed to create a better lifestyle for young people, especially us girlies.

Every young female out there reading this must be proud of who you are, if everyone was the same the world would be terribly boring and there would be no good-looking blokes to swoon over!!! Being an individual is important and models whatever shape or size will never be you, and you will never be them, so be happy and enjoy being you!

Question
When I look in magazines and see these models I think, I want to be like her with her golden hair, blue eyes and not one spot, I feel so down,

every other page in the magazine is plastered with faces of pretty girls!

Answer
Everyone is pretty in his or her own way, and you must not think that to be pretty you need to be a model. In everyday life every teenage girl will experience their first outbreak of spots, this is bad, I know, but everyone is in the same boat. Models cannot rule your life, be yourself.

Models are an image and they are not real, they are just made to perfection and this is not the human race, this is how we want people to be, but we cannot control what we look like, as we can food. You need to enjoy life as you, there is no harm in wanting to look good, but if you

feel that you are not eating and you see that being thin is the right way to be then please ring the helpline number on this page.

Remember, you are loved and liked for who you are, not for what you look like. So eat healthily and shop till ya drop!!!!

Contacts
EDA – The Eating Disorders Association, EDA Youth Helpline: 01603 765 050. Alternatively, see their address details on page 41.

• The above information is an extract from the Pupiline web site which can be found at www.pupiline.net

Ban skinny models? Fat chance, say magazines

By Tara Womersley

The Government's initiative to tackle eating disorders suffered fresh embarrassment yesterday after magazine editors denied that they had agreed to what was promoted as a principal part of its proposals.

A press conference after the Body Image Summit, chaired by Tessa Jowell, the minister for women, was told that there would be a self-regulatory group which would ban the use of anorexic models in magazines and ensure that models 'varied in shape and size'.

Yesterday a group of magazine editors who had been at the summit issued a statement saying that they had agreed to no such thing. The statement, with signatories including Alexandra Shulman, the editor of *Vogue*, and the designer Jasper Conran, said that the reports they had read made it seem 'that entirely another meeting must have taken place without us'.

It said that they had a close relationship with model agencies which they would inform if someone they were sent was 'sick in any way'. Miss Shulman said: 'I did not agree to self-regulation in any way or form. It's ridiculous to think that we just start flinging pictures of models at each other and saying that they are too thin.'

Laurie Kuhrt, from the Association of Model Agents, said: 'It is more than spin. It is actually a distortion of what happened at the meeting.' The statement followed a dispute over the role of the Broadcasting Standards Commission, which Miss Jowell said had offered to monitor the 'degree of diversity in the shapes of women on television'.

The commission denied this, saying merely that it was 'considering' asking for academic research into the area. Although fashion writers took part in the event, it was not open to the general media, which were briefed later at a press conference.

Obesity – the scale of the problem

Information from The Association for the Study of Obesity (ASO)

Obesity as a global problem

The number of people who are obese is rising rapidly throughout the world, making obesity one of the fastest developing public health problems. The World Health Organisation has described the problem of obesity as a 'worldwide epidemic'. It is estimated that around 250 million people worldwide are obese.

The USA has the highest prevalence of obesity. On average, over one-third of the adult population are obese, rising to more than 50% in some ethnic subgroups. Whilst other developed countries 'lag behind' the US they tend to follow the general trends. The rate of change in the UK is very similar to the US and this offers a frightening insight into the potential scale of the problem unless adequate strategies are adopted now to both prevent and treat obesity.

Obesity in the UK

In England, the prevalence of obesity has increased steadily during the last 50 years and since the 1980s the proportion of obese people has almost trebled. Currently, over 50% of the adult population are overweight (BMI>25kg/m^2) and 17% of men and 21% of women are obese (BMI>30kg/m^2). The prevalence of serious obesity increases with age. In 16-24-year-olds the prevalence is around 5% in both men and 10% in women. By age 55-64 years the prevalence is over 23% in men and 29% in women; a three- to four-fold increase.

Historically, obesity was associated with affluence and this is still the case across societies. Within developing countries such as India, Africa and South America obesity is a particular problem amongst the recently affluent classes, where being overweight is seen as a sign of prosperity. However, in developed countries there is an inverse relationship between obesity and social class, with a much greater proportion of obese people in the lower social classes than in professional groups. In the UK the prevalence of serious obesity increases from 15.1% in social class I to 31.4% in social class V.

(June 2000. These figures are the latest on the prevalence of obesity from the 1998 *Health Survey for England*, published by the Department of Health.)

Obesity in children

Less data is available about the prevalence of obesity in children. Moreover, due to difficulties in the definitions of overweight and obesity it is harder to make international comparisons.

What can be done?

Although obesity is a rapidly growing problem there are some signs that it is not irreversible. In some western European countries, e.g. the Netherlands and some parts of Scandinavia, the prevalence of obesity is far lower than that seen in the UK and is increasing much more slowly.

In the UK there are many local initiatives under way to prevent and treat obesity, however there is currently no national strategy. Some other countries have made national

plans to tackle the growing problem of obesity, for example 'Healthy Weight Australia'. Within many countries national Associations for the Study of Obesity bring together scientists and health professionals with an interest in obesity.

The Association for the Study of Obesity seeks to raise the awareness of obesity as a public health issue within the UK and to encourage research, and provides expert professional advice to Government and other organisations concerned with obesity issues.

On a global level, the International Obesity Task Force (IOTF) has been formed under the auspices of the International Association for the Study of Obesity (IASO). The IOTF includes obesity specialists from around the world. The main aims of the IOTF are:

- To raise awareness at all levels that obesity is a serious medical condition and a major global health problem.
- To develop policy recommendations for a coherent and effective global approach to manage and prevent obesity.
- To identify and implement strategies in collaboration with experts, professional organisations, patient groups and national health agencies. The IOTF web site can be found at www.iotf.org

• The above information is an extract from the Association for the Study of Obesity's web site which can be found at www.aso.org.uk/aso/frame.htm

Obesity: is it an eating disorder?

Information from ANRED – Anorexia Nervosa and Related Eating Disorders, Inc.

Like most things, obesity is a complex phenomenon about which it is dangerous to generalise. What is true for one person is not necessarily true for the next. Nevertheless, we shall try to make sense out of conflicting theories and give answers to people who struggle to maintain self-esteem in a world that seems to be obsessed with youth, thinness, and the perfect body – whatever that may be.

What is obesity?
A person with anorexia nervosa may define obesity as a weight gain of five pounds, from 89 to 94. A grandmother past menopause may call herself obese because she carries 165 pounds on her large-boned, muscular body. A modelling agency may talk about obesity when one of the women on the payroll puts 135 pounds on her 5'10" body.

None of these women is clinically obese. The anorexic and the model are underweight.

Men are split in their personal definitions of obesity. Many are just as concerned about overweight as women are, while others, frankly rotund, believe they are just fine, perfectly healthy, and universally attractive to potential romantic partners.

Many physicians consider a person to be obese only if s/he weighs more than 20% above expected weight for age, height, and body build. Morbid or malignant obesity is usually considered to be any weight in excess of 100 pounds above that expected for age, height, and build.

In recent years, the definition of expected, or healthy, weight has expanded to include more pounds per height in view of research that links reduced mortality (longer lives) with more weight than is currently considered fashionable.

How many Americans are obese?
Over half of American adults weigh more than they should. As many as 40 million Americans are overweight to the point of obesity, about one-third of all adults. The prevalence is increasing in all major socio-economic and ethnic groups, including children and younger adults between 25 and 44.

What are the causes of obesity?
- Consumption of more calories than are burned through work, exercise, and other activities.
- Inexpensive, tasty, plentiful food and a combination of leisure time, sedentary lifestyle, TV, and other 'activities' that require little or no physical effort.
- Attempts to medicate or escape emotional pain and distress. For various emotional reasons, including loneliness and depression, some people eat when their bodies do not need food.
- Diets and prolonged caloric restriction. When people try to make the body thinner than it is genetically programmed to be, it retaliates by becoming ravenous and vulnerable to binge eating. Ninety-eight per cent of dieters regain all the weight they manage to lose, plus about 10 extra pounds, within five years. Yo-yo dieting repeats the cycle of weight loss followed by ever-increasing weight gain when hunger ultimately wins.

> *For various emotional reasons, including loneliness and depression, some people eat when their bodies do not need food*

- Some individuals are obese because of specific biological problems such as malfunctioning thyroid or pituitary glands. Others may have physical problems or disabilities that severely limit or prohibit entirely exercise, strenuous work, and other physical activity.
- Researchers believe that in most cases obesity represents a complex relationship between genetic, psychological, physiological, metabolic, socioeconomic, and cultural factors.

The children of heavy parents are more likely to be heavy than the children of thin parents. If friends and family members offer comfort in the form of food, people will learn to deal with painful feelings by eating instead of using more effective strategies. Poor folks tend to be fatter than the affluent. People living in groups that frequently celebrate and socialise at get-togethers featuring tempting food tend to be fatter than those who do not. Some individuals eat great quantities of food, exercise moderately or not at all, and never seem to gain weight. Others walk past a bakery and gain ten pounds. No two people are the same, and no two obesity profiles are identical.

Health risks associated with obesity

- Hypertension (high blood pressure, a contributor to stroke and heart disease). Overweight young people (20-45) have a six times higher incidence of hypertension than do peers who are normal weight. Older obese folks seem to be at even greater risk.
- Diabetes. Even moderate obesity, especially when the extra fat is carried in the stomach and abdomen (instead of hips and thighs), increases the risk of non-insulin dependent diabetes mellitus (NIDDM) tenfold.
- Cardiovascular disease. Both the degree of obesity and the location of fat deposits contribute to the potential for heart and blood vessel disease. The fatter the person, the higher the risk. People who carry extra weight in the trunk area (stomach and abdomen) are at higher risk than

folks who store fat in hip and thigh deposits.
- Cancer. Obese men are at elevated risk of developing cancer of the colon, rectum, and prostate. Obese women are at elevated risk of developing cancer of the breast, cervix, uterus, and ovaries.
- Endocrine problems. Irregular menstrual cycles; other menstrual problems; and pregnancy complications, especially toxaemia and hypertension. Hormone imbalances of various kinds may contribute to, or be the result of, obesity.
- Gall bladder disease. Obese women 20-30 years old are at six times greater risk of gall bladder disease than their normal-weight peers. By age 60 almost one-third of obese women will have developed gall bladder disease.
- Lung and breathing problems. Obesity can impede the muscles that inflate and ventilate the lungs. Obese individuals may have to work hard to get enough air and over time may not be able to take in the oxygen needed by all body cells.
- Arthritis. Obese individuals are at increased risk of developing gouty arthritis, a distressingly painful disorder. Excess weight stresses vulnerable joints, in particular the back and knee, which may develop osteoarthritis, a mechanical rather than metabolic problem.

- Premature death. Research indicates that obese people die sooner than their normal weight peers.

Other problems associated with obesity

- Sleep disturbances including sleep apnoea (breathing stops for several seconds; then the person rouses, gasps, and struggles to catch breath; episodes may continue through the night).
- Inability to fully participate in recreational activities.
- Inability to compete effectively in sports and athletics; being picked last, or not at all, for team sports.
- Inability to perform some jobs; reduced job opportunities.
- Prejudice and discrimination in school and the workplace.
- Restricted social opportunities.
- Restricted opportunities for romantic relationships.
- Low self-esteem and body-image problems, related at least in part to prejudice and discrimination encountered in school, at work, and in social settings.

One important piece of good news

Obese people do not seem to have any more psychological problems, or more serious psychological problems, than folks of normal weight. The problems they do have are more likely a consequence of prejudice and

discrimination than a cause of overweight. In fact, several studies have suggested that the obese are significantly less anxious and depressed than normal-weight peers.

What can be done about obesity?

- The simplistic answer: eat less and exercise more.
- The realistic answer:
- Work with a physician to identify and correct any underlying medical, biological, or physiological problems contributing to excess weight.
- Check with a counsellor to see if you are using food for a purpose food cannot fulfil: love, comfort, escape, an antidote to boredom, and so forth. If you are self-medicating with food, work with the therapist to come up with better ways of managing stress, painful emotions, and problems.
- Don't ever diet or restrict calories when you are legitimately hungry. If you do, you will set yourself up to binge later.
- Eat normal, reasonable, moderate amounts of healthy foods. Emphasise fruits, vegetables, and whole grains. Don't cut out sweets and fats completely. If you do, you will crave and sneak them. Besides, your body needs the nutrients found in fats and carbohydrates. Just don't overdo it.
- Most important: exercise consistently. Get regular amounts of moderate, self-loving exercise. Start with a few minutes of walking and slowly extend the time until you can do 30-60 minutes a day, 3-5 days a week. If you haven't exercised in a while, be sure to check with your doctor first.
- Find a support system. Friends are great; so are support groups. There are both online and in-person opportunities.
- Be gentle and realistic with yourself. If everyone in your family is round and sturdy, chances are you will never be a supermodel – but you can be happy and healthy. Also remember that healthy, realistic

weight loss takes time. Losing one-half to one pound a week isn't very glamorous, but if you go any faster, you will make yourself hungry, and hunger will inevitably make you overeat.

How about diet pills and other weight-loss products? Surgery?

- Over-the-counter products. There are many items in drugstores and health food stores that claim to help people lose weight. None seems to be both safe and effective. The ones that are effective are only minimally so, and they have significant side effects and health risks. The ones that are safe don't seem to be very effective in helping folks lose weight and keep it off. Think about it: if there really were a safe and effective weight-loss product available over the counter, everyone in the United States would be thin. Our best advice: save your money.
- Prescription medications. In spite of a tremendous amount of research, there still is no magic pill that melts pounds away effortlessly. Obese people and their physicians had great hope for fen-phen, a combination stimulant and antidepressant, but those hopes were dashed when some of the people taking it developed potentially fatal heart problems. New medications are available, and more are in the pipeline. Talk to your doctor

about their pros and cons. For the time being at least, the steps outlined above in the section titled 'What Can Be Done About Obesity?' seem to be the safest and most effective way of reducing excess weight.
- Surgery. For some obese people, gastric bypass (stomach stapling and related techniques) may be a life-saving measure. The procedure is major surgery and is associated with risk of significant side effects and complications. For this reason it should be considered a treatment of last resort. Also, to be successful, the patient must co-operate with an entirely new way of eating and managing food. If nothing else has worked for you, and if your medical situation warrants such a drastic approach, talk to your physician to see if you might be a candidate for this procedure.

Please note: ANRED information is not a substitute for medical treatment or psychological care. For help with the physical and emotional problems associated with eating and exercise disorders, talk to your physician and a competent mental health professional.

• The above information is an extract from the ANRED – Anorexia Nervosa and Related Eating Disorders, Inc. web site which can be found at www.anred.com

© ANRED – Anorexia Nervosa and Related Eating Disorders, Inc.

Attitudes towards obesity

Information from MORI

With obesity on the increase, a MORI survey was conducted to establish public perceptions of obesity and the level of awareness of the causes and nature of the problem. The results confirmed fears that there is still a great deal of stigma associated with obesity. However, despite a lack of understanding about the causes of obesity, the message is finally getting through that obesity is a serious threat to our nation's health.

Obesity is a serious health risk

The survey revealed that 9 in 10 adults agree that obesity is a serious health risk.

The 55+ age group and the 25-34 age group are most likely to agree strongly that obesity is a serious health risk.

Stigma associated with obesity

9 out of 10 adults agree that there is a great deal of stigma associated with obesity.

The largest number of people who believe there is a great deal of stigma associated with obesity are in the age groups 25-34 / 35-44 / 45-54 years – over 9 in 10. The youngest and oldest age groups were least likely to recognise the stigma associated with obesity, although still more than 8 out of 10 people questioned did feel obesity is stigmatised.

By region, agreement that there is a great deal of stigma varies from 84% in London to 93% in Yorkshire & Humberside.

Causes of obesity – myths vs. reality

69% of the population considered eating too much high fat food to be one of the main causes of obesity with 65% thinking a lack of physical activity also contributes. But this still leaves around one-third of people who fail to recognise the importance of these factors in the increasing problem of obesity.

Women are significantly more likely to attribute other causes to the development of obesity, even though both sexes recognise the main culprits are eating too much high fat food and lack of physical activity.

Causes of obesity – lifestyle

Three in 10 of 15-24-year-olds did not recognise lack of physical activity as being a cause of obesity. 4 in 10 of 55+ age group also did not recognise it as a cause.

Seven in 10 people over the age of 24 say too much high fat food is a main cause of obesity. Scots are least likely to think this is a cause of obesity, with 4 in 10 failing to recognise it as a cause, while in the North East region of England only 2 in 10 failed to see the importance of this as a cause of obesity.

Nearly half of all Londoners say eating out too much is a main cause of obesity. In general, the older people get, the more likely they rate eating out as a possible cause.

Drinking too much beer is regarded by one-third of people as being a cause of obesity. People in the North East region of England rate drinking too much beer as a highly significant factor with half of those questioned in this area agreeing that this was a major cause of obesity.

Causes of obesity – biological

47% of people attribute medical reasons as a cause of obesity, when in fact obesity is often the cause of other medical problems. Younger people are more likely to cite medical reasons as a cause. Over half of the 15-24-year-olds questioned believe this. With increasing age this is less likely to be the case, with just under 4 in 10 of those aged 55+ attributing medical reasons as a cause of obesity.

More than 40% of people in each age group believe the person's state of mind is a cause of obesity, with the exception of 55+ years of age, in which only 27% think it is a main cause.

More than 1 in 4 of those over 25+ years believe that glandular problems are the main cause of obesity while just 1 in 6 of 15-24-year-olds gave this reason. Around 2 in 5 people of all age groups blame 'your family genes'.

Only 1 in 6 of 25-34-year-olds and just over 1 in 7 of 35-44-year-olds think pregnancy can cause obesity in women.

Technical note

The survey was conducted by MORI consisting of 2,098 adults aged 15+ who were interviewed face-to-face across 167 constituency-based sampling points. Data have been weighed to reflect the national population profile.

© Market & Opinion Research International (MORI)

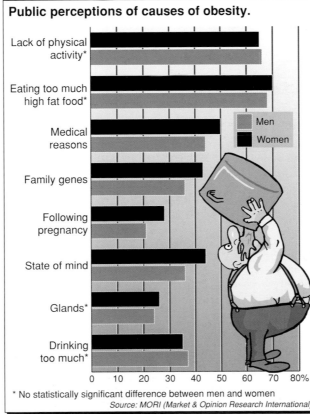

Myths vs. reality

Public perceptions of causes of obesity.

- Lack of physical activity*
- Eating too much high fat food*
- Medical reasons
- Family genes
- Following pregnancy
- State of mind
- Glands*
- Drinking too much*

Men
Women

0 10 20 30 40 50 60 70 80%

* No statistically significant difference between men and women
Source: MORI (Market & Opinion Research International)

The causes of obesity

Information from the National Centre For Eating Disorders

By Deanne Jade

Experts subscribe to one or other of two theories of weight increase, which we can identify as either the 'push' or the 'pull' theory. The pull theory suggests that weight is regulated by factors inside the body which pull food in – like, for example, there are lots of hungry fat cells waiting to be filled – and the push theory suggests there is something external in the family or the culture which pushes food in.

There is a lot of evidence for the push theory. After all, we live in a culture which celebrates food. Holidays are centred around eating. If you want to celebrate something you don't take your family to a salad bar. In our culture there are countless opportunities to eat together with countless messages telling you that you will be lacking something important – happiness even – if you do not eat. This 'supermarket environment' fosters fat. In a recent experiment with rats in the US, Kelly Brownell found that rats exposed to what he described as a supermarket environment gained weight to the point that they were 300% fatter than their natural weight. In addition we are much more sedentary than we used to be and researchers in Britain measured the effect of our sedentary lifestyle compared to that of 30 years ago, estimating that our lifestyle alone – despite the fact that we eat marginally fewer calories than we used to – accounts for a gain of 5-10lbs each year.

There is an evolutionary benefit conferred on people who are able to store fat. In olden times when food was scarce, it was fatter people – those who were able to store fat – who would survive illness and scarcity. Obesity would be rare in those times since periodic shortages made it impossible for weight to be gained progressively. However, although we live in the 20th century our bodies are still 'in the caves' so to speak, because culture has galloped ahead of our biological response to culture. This means that our bodies have not adapted to an environment in which there is plenty of food. Weight gain must result.

On the family level, push theory may operate. Some families foster overeating for emotional or cultural reasons, or simply from ignorance. Parents might teach bad habits, like forcing children to clear everything on their plates, eating quickly, or tie-in eating to relaxation such as watching television. Research indicates that eating in front of the TV may foster overweight because metabolism slows down when people are in a mild trance state and food energy is less likely to be converted to heat.

Stress is another factor in the external world which might lead to weight being gained. It is well known that obese binge eaters are more likely than thin people to eat in response to stress, loneliness or anger. This suggests a personality-led vulnerability to responding to push factors in the environment, and indeed stress-driven overeating is more common among deniers/avoiders. Overeating however is not a symptom of emotional distress – because if this were true the remedy would be to root it out. There are

> *Stress is another factor in the external world which might lead to weight being gained. It is well known that obese binge eaters are more likely than thin people to eat in response to stress, loneliness or anger*

many people with emotional problems who are not overweight, similarly there are many overweight people who try psychotherapy, yet who remain overweight despite addressing their emotional issues. Obviously something else is going on.

Evidence for the pull theory
A) Fat cell biology
A lot of work is being done on the biology of fat cells. Researchers in Sweden recently discovered that people tend to drop out of weight loss programmes – not when they had attained their target weight but when their fat cells had reached normal size. For two people of the same height, this could occur at greatly different weights. This might be so because one person may have more fat cells than the other.

Overweight children and very obese adults are known to have more fat cells than usual. This is called hyperplastic obesity. Fat cells are usually formed at two critical periods of a person's life – in early childhood and at puberty. We now know that new fat cells can be formed at any time of life if weight is gained rapidly or if fat cells grow to over 50% of their normal size.

Similarly if people try to reduce their weight to the point where their fat cells shrink below their normal size they start to behave as if they are starving (even if they eat fairly well) and they display all the usual symptomology of people with eating disorders – craving, being obsessional and performing rituals etc. So there is obviously some kind of biological pressure to keep fat cells at approximately their normal size, even if technically this means that a person may be culturally 'overweight'. This provides evidence for the Set Point theory which is described below.

B) Set Point theory
Further support for the pull effect comes from set weight theory.

Question – do we all have a biological mechanism which determines what weight we are going to be stable at and will pull food into our mouths until we have attained that weight? If you give healthy rats as much rat food as they can eat (not the supermarket diet) their weight remains remarkably stable. Also, look at people who lose weight – 97% regain all the weight they have lost, magically settling to more or less what they were before the diet. Good evidence for set weight. But this system breaks down at times – remember the rats in the supermarket environment, gaining weight to a level far in excess of their normal weight. So we can say that the environment will have an effect on our genetic levels of control.

As I have described elsewhere, although there is strong evidence for a set weight experts now feel that it is not an exact level of weight but rather a broad band and the position we take on that band will be affected by our lifestyle, food choices and exercise levels, and our age and gender.

C) Metabolism

Overweight people often claim that they have a slow metabolism, which we could ascribe to the pull theory. Food is pulled in but it cannot be burned. Metabolism is the rate at which we burn energy and is also affected by age and gender, body musculature and exercise levels. There is also a very important component of metabolism which is influenced by the food we eat and by our dieting history. It is true that metabolism varies among individuals – by up to 100 calories daily. Although there is evidence that overweight children can burn energy at a slower level than slim children (perhaps because slim children feel more comfortable at running around) overweight adults do NOT have slower metabolisms – they have higher metabolic levels consistent with their additional body weight. Note that exercise has a profound effect on metabolism mostly due to changes in cell response to insulin and dieting has a strong effect on metabolic rate.

D) Genes

Another possible pull factor is in the genes. Is overweight hereditary? Well yes, it does run in families. Only 20% of children with no obese parents become overweight; 60% of children with one parent, and this rises to 80% of children who have two overweight parents. Could it just be bad eating habits being passed on? The answer may lie in adoption studies in Denmark where the weight of adoptees was compared to their natural and their adoptive parents. The weight of children as they grew corresponded most closely to their natural parents. Even more interesting were the studies done with identical twins raised apart. Thin separated twins grew up identical in size and weight. Overweight separated twins grew up overweight but there was much more variability in their body size, corresponding to other factors such as environment. From these studies we can estimate that genetics accounts for up to 70% of an influence on obesity.

E) Glands

Are they a pull factor? Glandular problems account for less than 5% of cases of obesity.

After looking at all these factors, while we cannot be specific about the causes of weight gain, we can at least dismiss some of the myths about fat people, namely 'fat people are greedy'. There is no evidence that fat people are greedy. Fat people need to eat more than thin people to support higher energy needs due to their additional weight. What is true is that fat people are more likely to turn to food in times of stress than thin people and this may be due to personality factors but we can speculate that due to cultural and social pressures which lead fat people to feel bad about themselves they may be driven into ways of thinking which support this kind of avoidance behaviour.

'I was born to be fat.' Twin studies might lead people to despair – 'what's the use, I can't do anything about it?' It is unfair, but it doesn't mean that weight cannot be controlled. All you inherit is a tendency to put on weight, careful eating and exercise habits lower the range at which you will settle.

'Fat people are lazy.' Many fat people do not exercise due to embarrassment or because they find it uncomfortable, but many people do not exercise for different reasons.

'Fat people are responsible for their condition.' This kind of thinking is unfair and misplaced.

So who does need to lose weight? Certainly not as many people as are concerned about it. Recent surveys show that almost 50% of people are concerned about their weight and half as many are trying to do something about it right now, even including large numbers of children, and people who acknowledge that they are not strictly overweight. There is a massive obesity phobia in the culture.

4 out of 10 women say that they are terrified about the prospect of gaining weight and children as young as 6 choose as a potential playmate a child who is disabled rather than one who is fat. The amount of distress in some women being half a stone over their ideal weight bears no relationship to the effect it has on their looks. Perhaps these biases arise from the importance we place in our culture on self-denial and self-control.

So who needs to lose weight?
Experts generally agree that health risks set in at about 30lbs excess weight and the risks of overweight are as follows:
- hypertension risk 6x normal
- coronary artery disease 3x normal
- diabetes 4x normal
- cancer – obese men are significantly at risk with higher rates of colon prostate and rectal cancer. Women have higher risk of bowel, gall bladder and breast cancer at 30% overweight.

For people with upper body fat the health risks set in sooner.

Conclusion
Obesity is a complex issue. There are lots of different types of obesity with different causes.

It has different physiological and psychological manifestations and cannot be explained by a single label such as 'gluttony'.

There is no single guaranteed treatment programme for obesity and individuals must be matched to treatments and any programme undertaken must be sensitive to personal motivation and the personal factors which affect long-term commitment. The search is still on for a safe drug therapy which will reduce body fat, it being recognised that such a programme will have to be continued for the lifetime of an individual.

© Deanne Jade, National Centre For Eating Disorders 1999

Compulsive (over)eating

The most common element surrounding all eating disorders is the inherent presence of a low self-esteem

People suffering with compulsive overeating have what is characterised as an 'addiction' to food, using food and eating as a way to hide from their emotions, to fill a void they feel inside, and to cope with daily stresses and problems in their lives.

People suffering with this eating disorder tend to be overweight, are usually aware that their eating habits are abnormal, but find little comfort because of society's tendency to stereotype the 'overweight' individual. Words like 'just go on a diet' are as emotionally devastating to a person suffering compulsive overeating as 'just eat' can be to a person suffering anorexia. A person suffering as a compulsive overeater is at health risk for a heart attack, high blood pressure and cholesterol, kidney disease and/or failure, arthritis and bone deterioration, and stroke.

Men and women who are compulsive overeaters will sometimes hide behind their physical appearance, using it as a blockade against society (common in victims of sexual abuse). They feel guilty for not being 'good enough', shame for being overweight, and generally have a very low self-esteem . . . they use food and eating to cope with these feelings, which only leads into the cycle of feeling them tenfold and trying to find a way to cope again. With a low self-esteem and often constant need for love and validation he/she will turn to obsessive episodes of bingeing and eating as a way to forget the pain and the desire for affection.

It is important to remember that most eating disorders, though their signs and symptoms may be different, share a great number of common causes and emotional aspects.

From Tom . . .
I suppose it is ironic that I work at a hospital. I was married to an alcoholic . . . how nice it would be to have a simple addiction like booze . . . you give it up and you are recovering. But you have to eat. Well I eat . . . when I'm hungry . . . when I'm full . . . when I'm anxious . . . when I'm happy . . . when I'm sad . . . well you get the idea. Food, the friend that never fails.

With a low self-esteem he/she will turn to obsessive episodes of bingeing and eating

When I was a kid I was trained that food made it all better. When we were totally broke my mum would cook the most. She was a compulsive feeder so I became a compulsive eater.

Every diet has failed. I am a lifer on Weight Watchers, I have been through Nutra System. But it's not about the weight . . . it's about the inability to deal with feelings and emotions . . . about using a bowl of pasta or a pound of m&ms as a narcotic to stem the pain.

That's what compulsive overeating is.

I cry because it makes me overweight and no one sees the real me inside. I try to show the real me and I think that people don't like me because I am overweight. Another catch-22 or chicken-and-egg thing. I see my son gaining weight and I grieve. I want out . . . but then I realise that there is no out . . . only control . . . and control is harder than being in or out.

• The above information is an extract from the Something Fishy Web site on Eating Disorders which can be found at www.something-fishy.org

Understanding obesity

Information from the European Food Information Council (EUFIC)

Over a third of the population of many European countries is overweight according to health experts. Obesity, or overweight, is usually measured as the relationship between weight and height, called the 'Body Mass Index' (BMI). For an individual, the BMI is determined by dividing the person's weight in kilograms by the square of his or her height in metres (kg/m^2). It is widely accepted that a BMI of greater than 30 reflects obesity.

In recent decades the prevalence of obesity has increased. For example, in 1980, obesity occured in 8% of women and 6% of men in Great Britain; by 1993, this had increased to 16% of women and 13% of men.

The risks of obesity

Obesity and overweight are important health concerns since they are associated with an increased risk of mortality. Although premature mortality is hardly increased in the moderately overweight (BMI 25-30), the risk of disability, mainly from musculoskeletal and cardiovascular diseases, is significantly increased.

With obesity, however, it is well documented that the risk of mortality rises exponentially as BMI exceeds 30. Obesity is associated with several specific health risks including an increased incidence of hypertension (high blood pressure), increased non-insulin-dependent (maturity onset) diabetes and high blood levels of cholesterol and other lipids. Corrected for these risk factors, obesity in itself has been reported to be an independent risk factor for heart disease.

The distribution of fat on a person's body is another important factor. Fat or adipose tissue tends to accumulate – centrally around the waist (visceral fat), or more generally, including on the hips and limbs, where the fat is said to be 'peripheral' (or 'subcutaneous', i.e. under the skin). The result is to give people what is described as an apple or pear shape respectively. Individuals with central fat distribution have a higher waist-to-hip ratio (WHR) and are more likely to have disorders of fat metabolism and to develop diabetes and coronary heart disease than those who store fat peripherally with a lower WHR. This effect is independent of the Body Mass Index. The higher rate of coronary heart disease in males compared to females may be explained in part by the well-documented higher visceral fat levels in males.

Finally, the obese also carry an enhanced risk of certain types of cancers, such as those of the large intestine and the breast.

Balancing energy intake and energy use

Body weight maintenance over a period of time occurs when:
Energy expenditure=energy intake.

A person's daily energy intake – measured in kilocalories (kcal) – comes from the energy-containing nutrients in food, i.e. fat, alcohol, carbohydrate and protein. These nutrients contribute 9,7,4 and 4 kcal respectively per gram of pure nutrient consumed.

Energy expenditure results from:
- The basal metabolic rate (BMR) is the energy required to maintain all body tissues including muscles and organs and to regulate body temperature. It comprises approximately 60-70% of daily energy intake in sedentary individuals. Contrary to popular belief, BMR in obese people is higher than that found in lean individuals, which reflects the greater total amount of metabolically active tissue of obese persons.
- The thermic effect of food (TEF) or the energy which is lost as heat following a meal; this comprises up to 10% of daily energy intake.
- Physical activity which is the most variable component of energy expenditure in individuals. In sedentary people, exercise may constitute approximately 15% of total energy expenditure, whereas an individual who regularly exercises may expend up to 30% of his or her total daily energy output in this manner.

With these facts in mind, it is useful to look at the likely causes of the recent increase in overweight and obesity.

The effects of heredity

There is no doubt that obesity has a genetic component although research has not been able to pinpoint a specific metabolic defect in man. In the past few years, a number of potential differences in metabolism have been observed. For example, obese people seem to be less able to mobilise the fat stored in their adipose tissue.

It is clear, however, that genetic factors interact with environmental influences. Also genetic factors could not be responsible for the significant increase in obesity during the past 15 years since the gene pool of indigenous Europeans cannot possibly have changed significantly in such a short period. Clearly factors other than genetics have been at work.

In the past, many people who had weight problems claimed that they ate very little, but recently it has been found that most people, especially those who are obese, tend to under-report the amount they eat. In order to gain weight, a person's energy intake must exceed his or her energy expenditure.

In addition to the quantity of food consumed, the composition of food is an important risk factor for overweight and obesity.

The fat content of the diet

Many studies have demonstrated an association between body fatness and the fat content of the diet. It is generally accepted that the high-fat content of the average European diet results in the consumption of more calories than people generally realise; the most important reason why high-fat diets have such a substantial impact on body weight is thought to be that they are very energy dense, having a high kcal (energy) value per gram of food. Therefore, it is easy to consume more than is necessary to meet energy needs. Cotton and Blundell (1993) refer to this as 'passive over-consumption'. Furthermore, researchers have reported that fat is less able to satisfy the appetite than is carbohydrate or protein. Finally, fat is the last metabolic fuel in the body to be oxidised for the provision of energy – the body preferring

In addition to the quantity of food consumed, the composition of food is an important risk factor for overweight and obesity

carbohydrate and protein as fuel. In short, it is easy to eat too much fat and not too easy to burn it off.

This has been demonstrated in an experimental study in which young, lean men were given three diets with either 20%, 40% or 60% of the calories contributed by fat. (Typical European diets contain about 40% calories from fat.) The men did not know which diet they were eating and the foods were cleverly disguised to avoid detection of the changes. When served the highest-fat diet, the men ate more food than they needed without realising they were doing so. Conversely, when they ate the lowest-fat diet, they ate less than they needed. When the experiment was conducted with the men maintaining a sedentary existence in a metabolic laboratory, they also ate too much when consuming the 40% fat calories diet. However, if they were allowed to go about their normal daily activities then they ate less than they needed and went into negative energy balance on the 40% fat calories diet. Thus, the typical European diet (containing about 40% calories from fat) can easily lead to overeating when people have a sedentary existence.

In a separate but similar experiment to the free-living experiment described above, all the foods were prepared so that the diets had 20, 40, or 60% calories from fat but had the same energy density (that is the same kcal/g). Here the men did not over-consume energy on any of the diets and succeeded in maintaining their energy balance. This indicates that the reason high-fat diets are more fattening is mainly because they have a high energy density.

Conversely, it has been readily demonstrated that low-fat, high-carbohydrate diets result in spontaneous IC weight loss.

Sugar and other carbohydrates in the diet. It also seems that diets high in sugars are not more fattening than diets high in carbohydrates in general. It is well known that there is an inverse relationship between energy from carbohydrate and energy from fat in the diet. This means that as the proportion of energy from fat in the diet decreases, the proportion of energy from carbohydrate increases. Furthermore, this relationship extends to sugar. A recent, large epidemiological study showed that the lowest sugar consumers were two to four times more likely to be obese than were the highest sugar consumers.

Apart from the differing effects of carbohydrates and fat on appetite and food intake, several other factors differentiate the body's two main fuel sources:

- The body more readily metabolises carbohydrates (and protein and alcohol); dietary fat tends to go straight into fat stores. This idea is supported by the fact that human fat stores have the same composition as the fat eaten in the diet;

- The energy expended to store dietary fat as body fat requires only about 3% of the ingested calories; on the other hand, storing carbohydrate as body fat requires about 23% of the ingested calories. This is probably why the body does not usually convert carbohydrates into fat;

- Protein and carbohydrates have a greater thermic effect (TEF) than does fat, i.e. the higher the protein and carbohydrate content of a meal, the greater the amount of heat generated immediately after the meal. In practice, however, this effect is probably small.

Do taste preferences play a role?

A preference for a sweet taste is innate, with sensory preferences being higher in children and declining by adulthood. It is unlikely that the preference for fat is innate. The degree of overweight has been reported to be negatively correlated with preferences for sweet taste, that is, people with a greater preference for sweet taste are less likely to be obese. On the other hand, several studies have reported a preference for high-fat foods by obese and formerly obese individuals.

It has been suggested that the palatable combination of sugar and fat contributes a considerable proportion of energy to the diet, leading to overeating and excess energy intake. Some studies have implied that the presence of sugar in combination with fat in certain foods leads to their greater consumption. An example of relative importance of foods containing both sugar and fat in the adult diet is given by calculations using the Dietary and Nutritional Survey of British Adults, and the British National Food Survey adjusted to include foods consumed outside the home. These calculations demonstrate that only 14.2% of total sugar and 16% of total fat intake in the household diet is composed of foods in a sugar-fat combination.

Similar observations can be made for diets from a number of other European countries including Ireland and the Basque country.

The (beneficial) impact of physical activity

In spite of the increase in obesity over the last decade, there has actually been a parallel decline in food energy intake. According to UK National Food Survey data (corrected for energy intake outside the home), average per capita energy intake has decreased by 20% between 1970 and 1990.

Prentice and Jebb (1995) have stated that the data from the National Food Survey are corroborated by individual studies on food energy intake. They also concluded that the percentage of energy derived from fat, although high, has remained stable over those 20 years. Therefore, energy intake and fat intake cannot alone explain the apparent epidemic of obesity. In affluent societies, few people are engaged in physically arduous jobs and most domestic situations are now characterised by labour-saving devices and central heating. None of these changes are readily quantifiable, but

it is clear that most adults, whether lean or obese, are sedentary.

In the UK, two questionnaire surveys of activity found that 7 out of 10 men and 8 out of 10 women were physically inactive.

While children in Scotland in the 1980s were about the same weight and height as those in the 1930s, their energy intakes were about one-sixth and one-quarter lower for boys and girls, respectively. This indicates that children use less energy — i.e., are less physically active — today than previously. Using modern techniques to measure energy expenditure, Livingstone reported that the amount of energy expended on physical activity declined with age in children and adolescents.

This indicated a worrying trend towards a sedentary lifestyle in adolescence.

It is notoriously difficult to measure physical activity accurately and few studies have attempted to do so. Thus Prentice and Jebb decided to look at data on television viewing and the use of cars as a proxy measure for inactivity. The average UK person now spends 26 hours per week watching TV compared with just 13 hours in the 1960s. Furthermore, TV viewing hours are greater in the lower socio-economic groups who also have a higher prevalence of obesity. Physical activity does not offer a cure for obesity. Experts, however, do recommend a combination of diet and exercise, because exercise helps reduce the loss of lean body mass which occurs during dieting thus helping maintain the body's basal metabolic rate, in particular, low intensity exercise such as brisk walking favours fat oxidation; as there is some evidence that fat

oxidation is impaired in obese and post-obese people, this type of exercise may be particularly beneficial to such people.

Thus most experts now recommend that everyone should try to increase his or her daily amount of physical activity. Even the increase in physical activity associated with many small changes in habits such as using the stairs instead of the lift, walking to shops or moving around the office sometimes, instead of sitting all day, can make a significant difference to total energy expenditure. For those already active, using a bicycle instead of the car or participating in some planned activities in leisure time can also help maintain a healthy body weight.

Apart from a possible role in preventing obesity, physical activity has other benefits. It affects metabolism and increases protective high density lipoprotein cholesterol. It improves the body's handling of dietary fat and enhances the body's ability to use glucose, thereby reducing the risk of diabetes in susceptible individuals. There is also increasing evidence that maintaining an adequate level of physical activity throughout life may help reduce the incidence of the so-called diseases of affluence such as coronary heart disease and certain cancers.

Conclusion

It is widely recognised that in spite of the fact that people have a high awareness about the importance of diet, obesity and overweight are on the increase. Adjusting to a diet with a lower proportion of fat than our typical European cuisine is still seen as an important part of a healthy life-style. However, the important new message is that keeping physically active throughout life will benefit everyone in terms of general health and should also help in the fight against the increasing problem of overweight and obesity

• The above information is an extract from the European Food Information Council (EUFIC) web site which can be found at www.eufic.org

Food and emotions

Information from the European Food Information Council (EUFIC)

Eating has never been and never will be simply about satisfying physical hunger. We eat not only to quell a rumbling stomach, but also to satisfy the appetite and deal with emotions.

From the moment a parent first offers a biscuit or sweet to comfort and quiet a child, food becomes a way of nourishing the soul as well as the body. From the earliest age food is used to celebrate, to calm, to relieve boredom or depression and to comfort in times of sadness and emotional distress. Such behaviour is not unusual. Having a piece of birthday cake when it would be anti-social to refuse, rewarding yourself with some chocolate or a few biscuits after finishing a daunting job, having a glass of wine or beer to be sociable, are all normal practices.

The problem comes when emotionally driven food habits take over from healthy eating and result in uncontrolled weight gains.

Recognising the fact that solving the vast majority of people's weight problems is not about simply providing 1,500-calorie-a-day diets and exercise plans, many dieting experts are now including behaviour modification techniques in their various approaches to weight loss and weight maintenance.

Uncovering emotional eating is the first step in the road to recovery. The following questions and suggestions may help to find the solutions to emotionally driven weight gain.

Q. Do you eat when you aren't hungry?

Keep a food diary to find out what, how much and when you eat and the emotion or situation that triggered it. Being aware of the reasons may help you to address them. If you are angry about something, work out why and try to deal with it. If you are sad, sit down, write out why you are sad and see if there are ways of making yourself happy without turning to food.

Q. Do you crave certain foods?

When the craving next hits, be aware of what is happening and know that if you can ride it out, it will eventually pass. Have a list of things you can do to divert your attention and help it pass. Make a phone call, go for a walk, have a bath or make a hot drink.

The problem comes when emotionally driven food habits take over from healthy eating and result in uncontrolled weight gains

---

Q. Do you eat because you are depressed and can never live up to the media's view of the perfect image?

Change your goals and start to eat well and exercise regularly, not to look like a super model but to be fitter, leaner, slimmer and to feel good about yourself.

Combining clear and simple guides to good nutrition with effective and practical advice on exercise is for many just half of the solution when it comes to permanent weight loss. Understanding the reasons for overeating, tackling them and finding practical strategies for change will enhance the likelihood of attaining your weight loss goals.

© European Food Information Council (EUFIC)

Understanding food addiction and compulsive eating

What is food addiction?

Food addiction may take the form of 'comfort eating' due to stress or unhappiness but may also be more severe, leading to severe obesity and its various medical complications. Severe obesity is defined medically as being 20% or more above average weight. About one in five of the population is mildly overweight and about one in a hundred severely overweight. Eating disorders are, of course, not only problems of shape, size or weight, but are often ways in which people (generally but not invariably women) try to deal with painful emotions and fears by over-control or distortion of their eating patterns. They then become trapped. Treatment, therefore, is about help with self-esteem, self-confidence and emotional growth as well as help in restoring normal eating patterns and physical health.

How would I know if I or a relative or friend had food addiction or a compulsive eating disorder?

Compulsive eating and excessive weight are matters which should be taken seriously, although many women in our society (and increasingly men) seem to be constantly struggling with diets and efforts to lose weight. Some sections of the media and the 'slimming industry' seem to encourage this.

People who have a serious weight problem have often gone through a number of different diets or been to various slimming organisations without achieving benefit or long-term weight loss. There may be complicated emotional reasons for their compulsive eating, for which they need expert help.

© 2000 Priory Healthcare

ADDITIONAL RESOURCES

You might like to contact the following organisations for further information. Due to the increasing cost of postage, many organisations cannot respond to enquiries unless they receive a stamped, addressed envelope.

ANRED (Anorexia Nervosa and Related Eating Disorders, Inc.)
Post Office Box 5102
Eugene
OR 97405
USA
Web site: www.anred.com
ANRED is a non-profit organisation that provides free and low-cost information about anorexia nervosa, bulimia nervosa, binge eating disorder (sometimes called compulsive eating), and other less well-known eating and weight disorders. Their material includes details about recovery and prevention.

Association for the Study of Obesity (ASO)
20 Brook Meadow Close
Woodford Green
Essex
IG8 9NR
Tel: 020 8503 2042
Fax: 020 8503 2442
Web site: www.aso.org.uk
Promotes medical research into the causes, prevention and treatment of obesity. Facilitates contact between individuals and organisations interested in any aspect of the problem of obesity and body weight regulation. Produces publications.

British Medical Association (BMA)
BMA House
Tavistock Square
London
WC1H 9JP
Tel: 020 7387 4499
Fax: 020 7383 6400
E-mail: enquiries@bma.org.uk
Web site: www.bma.org.uk
The British Medical Association is the voice of the medical profession, speaking for doctors in the UK and abroad and providing services for its members. It is in constant touch with government ministers and departments, Members of Parliament and other influential bodies, putting across the profession's views on health policy. Please note that the BMA does not have the resources to deal with individual enquiries. However, they will respond to teachers' enquiries.

British Nutrition Foundation (BNF)
High Holborn House
52-54 High Holborn
London
WC1V 6RQ
Tel: 020 7404 6504
Fax: 020 7404 6747
E-mail: postbox@nutrition.org.uk
Web site: www.nutrition.org.uk
The BNF is an independent charity which provides reliable information and advice on nutrition and related health matters. They produce a wide range of leaflets, briefing papers and books. Ask for their publications list.

Eating Disorders Association (EDA)
1st Floor, Wensum House
103 Prince of Wales Road
Norwich
Norfolk
NR1 1DW
Tel: 01603 619090
Fax: 01603 664915
E-mail: info@edauk.com
Web site: www.edauk.com
Eating Disorders Association is a national charity offering help, support and information to people whose lives are affected by eating disorders, in particular anorexia and bulimia nervosa. It aims to campaign to improve standards of treatment and care and to raise awareness of eating disorders and related issues. Telephone helplines 01603 621 414 (helpline – open 9.00am to 6.30pm weekdays) 01603 765 050 (youthline callers 18 & under – open 4.00pm to 6.00pm weekdays).

European Food Information Council (EUFIC)
1 Place des Pyramides 75001
Paris
France
Tel: 00 33 140 20 44 40
Fax: 00 33 140 20 44 41
E-mail: eufic@eufic.org
Web site: www.eufic.org
EUFIC is a non-profit-making organisation based in Paris. It has been established to provide science-based information on foods and food-related topics, i.e. nutrition and health, food safety and quality and biotechnology in food for the attention of European consumers. It publishes regular newsletters, leaflets, reviews, case studies and other background information on food issues.

National Centre for Eating Disorders
54 New Road
Esher
Surrey
KT10 9NU
Tel: 01372 469493
E-mail: ncfed.globalnet.co.uk
Web site: www.eating-disorders.org.uk
The National Centre For Eating Disorders, established in 1984, is an independent organisation set up to provide solutions for all eating problems, compulsive or 'binge' eating, 'failed' or yo-yo dieting, bulimia and anorexia.

Royal College of Psychiatrists
17 Belgrave Square
London
SW1X 8PG
Tel: 020 7235 2351
Fax: 020 7235 1935
E-mail: rcpsych@rcpsych.ac.uk
Web site: www.rcpsych.ac.uk
Produces an excellent series of free leaflets on various aspects of mental health. Supplied free of charge but a stamped, addressed envelope is required.

INDEX

Independence Web News

| Back | Forward | Home | Reload | Images | Open | Print | Find | Stop |

| Live Home Page | Search | Computer | Support | System |

* * * * *

The Internet has been likened to shopping in a supermarket without aisles. The press of a button on a Web browser can bring up thousands of sites but working your way through them to find what you want can involve long and frustrating on-line searches.

And unfortunately many sites contain inaccurate, misleading or heavily biased information. Our researchers have therefore undertaken an extensive analysis to bring you a selection of quality Web site addresses.

Eating Disorders Association (EDA)
www.edauk.com
An essential site to visit for anyone wanting detailed UK-based information on eating disorders including: what causes eating disorders?, eating disorders in young people, advice/help, poems, reading lists etc.

British Nutrition Foundation (BNF)
www.nutrition.org.uk
Entering 'eating disorders' in the Search field brought up 146 articles. Well worth a visit.

Obesity.com
www.obesity.com
Obesity.com, a US based site, is dedicated to providing practical, up-to-the-minute information about weight loss and obesity. The site provides practical information that supports healthy and practical weight management and weight loss.

ANRED (Anorexia Nervosa and Related Eating Disorders, Inc.)
www.anred.com
ANRED is a non-profit organisation that provides information about anorexia nervosa, bulimia nervosa, binge eating disorder, and other less well known eating and weight disorders.

Association for the Study of Obesity (ASO)
www.aso.org.uk
Provides factsheets on current research and professional opinion relating to obesity.

Something Fishy Website on Eating Disorders
www.something-fishy.com/ed.htm
An impressive web site on eating disorders. It includes a vast amount of information, on anorexia, bulimia, overeating and other eating disorders. Mostly US-based information but well worth a visit.

ACKNOWLEDGEMENTS

The publisher is grateful for permission to reproduce the following material.

While every care has been taken to trace and acknowledge copyright, the publisher tenders its apology for any accidental infringement or where copyright has proved untraceable. The publisher would be pleased to come to a suitable arrangement in any such case with the rightful owner.

Chapter One: Eating Disorders
Eating disorders, © The Florence Nightingale Hospitals, *Worries about weight*, © The Royal College of Psychiatrists, *The children who starve themselves to cope with school*, © Elizabeth Hartley-Brewer, *Men get eating disorders too*, © The Eating Disorders Association (EDA), *High-flying schools put girls at greater risk of eating disorders*, © The Independent Newspapers Ltd 2000, *Definitions*, ©ANRED – Anorexia Nervosa and Related Eating Disorders, Inc., *Distorted perceptions*, © Something Fishy Music & Publishing, 1996-2000, *Common misconceptions*, © Something Fishy Music & Publishing, 1996-2000, *Warning signs*, © ANRED – Anorexia Nervosa and Related Eating Disorders, Inc., *Helping a friend or relative*, © The Eating Disorders Association (EDA).

Chapter Two: Body Image
Body image in our time, © The National Centre for Eating Disorders, *Eating disorders, body image and the media*, © British Medical Association (BMA), *Body image and eating disorders*, © British Nutrition Foundation (BNF), *Thin stars on TV 'put pressure on the young'*, © Telegraph Group Limited, London 2000, *Pressure to be thin affecting young women's self-esteem*, © Cabinet Office, Crown copyright is reproduced with the permission of the Controller of Her Majesty's Stationery Office, *Society and eating disorders*, © Colleen Thompson, *What you should know*, © The National Centre for Eating Disorders, *Looking good*, © Pupiline, *Ban skinny models? Fat chance, say magazines*, © Telegraph Group Limited, London 2000.

Chapter Three: Obesity
Obesity – the scale of the problem, © The Association for the Study of Obesity (ASO), *Obesity: is it an eating disorder?*, © ANRED – Anorexia Nervosa and Related Eating Disorders, Inc., *Attitudes towards obesity*, © Market & Opinion Research International (MORI), *The causes of obesity*, © The National Centre for Eating Disorders, *Compulsive (over)eating*, © Something Fishy Music & Publishing, 1996-2000, *Understanding obesity*, © European Food Information Council (EUFIC), *Food and emotions*, © European Food Information Council (EUFIC), *Understanding food addiction and compulsive eating*, © 2000 Priory Healthcare.

Photographs and illustrations:
Pages 1, 3, 12, 14, 18, 26, 32: Pumpkin House, pages 6, 9, 16, 21, 24, 29, 31, 35, 37: Simon Kneebone.

Craig Donnellan
Cambridge
January, 2001